CATALYST G

A framework for success

Carol Chapman

Moira Sheehan

Martin Stirrup

Mark Winterbottom

Heinemann

Inspiring generations

Contents

T indicates Think about spread

Introduction

Welcome to Catalyst

This is the third of three books designed to help you learn all the science ideas you need during Key Stage 3. We hope you'll enjoy the books as well as learning a lot from them.

This book has twelve units which each cover a different topic. The units have two types of pages:

Learn about:

Most of the double-page spreads in a unit introduce and explain new ideas about the topic. They start with a list of these so that you can see what you are going to learn about.

Think about:

Some units have a double-page spread called Think about. You will work in pairs or small groups and discuss your answers to the questions. These pages will help you understand how scientists work and how ideas about science develop.

On the pages there are these symbols:

a Quick questions scattered through the pages help you check your knowledge and understanding of the ideas as you go along, for example,

> **a** **Use the particle model to explain why the liquid will not squash.**

Questions

The questions at the end of the spread help you check you understand all the important ideas.

For your notes:

These list the important ideas from the spread to help you learn, write notes and revise.

Do you remember?

These remind you of what you already know about the topic.

Did you know?

These tell you interesting or unusual things, such as the history of some science inventions and ideas.

After the twelve units, A–L, this book contains a lot of extra material to help you get the best results in your SATs.

First, there are six double-page booster spreads to help you fully understand the five key ideas in science (cells, interdependence, particles, forces and energy). Your teacher will suggest you work through them to improve your knowledge and move up to the next level.

As you work through this pupil book these small symbols on some pages link to the booster spreads at the back of the book.

Next, there are five double-page revision spreads. The first one has some ideas about how best to revise for your SATs. The next four have SAT questions with notes from an examiner giving you suggestions about how to get the best possible marks.

At the back of the book:

Glossary

All the important scientific words in the text appear in bold type. They are listed with their meanings in the Glossary at the back of the book. Look there to remind yourself what they mean.

Index

There is an Index at the very back of the book, where you can find out which pages cover a particular topic.

Activities to help or check your learning:

Your teacher may give you these activities from the teacher's materials which go with the course:

Unit map

You can use this to think about what you already know about a topic. You can also use it to revise a topic before a test or exam.

Starters

When you start a lesson this is a short activity to introduce what you are going to learn about.

Activity

There are different types of activities, including investigations, that your teacher can give you to help with the topics in each spread in the pupil book.

Plenaries

At the end of a lesson your teacher may give you a short activity to summarise what you have learnt.

Homework

At the end of a lesson the teacher may give you one of the homework sheets that go with the lesson. This will help you to review and revise what you learnt in the lesson.

Pupil checklist

This is a checklist of what you should have learnt to help you with your revision.

Test yourself

You can use this quiz at the end of each unit to see what you are good at and what you might need to revise.

End of unit test Green

This helps you and your teacher check what you learnt during the unit, and measures your progress and success.

Heinemann Educational Publishers
Halley Court, Jordan Hill, Oxford OX2 8EJ
Part of Harcourt Education

Heinemann is a registered trademark of
Harcourt Education Limited

© Carol Chapman, Moira Sheehan, Martin Stirrup, Mark Winterbottom 2004

First published 2004

08 07 06 05
10 9 8 7 6 5

British Library Cataloguing in Publication Data is available
from the British Library on request.

10-digit ISBN: 0 435 76051 3
13-digit ISBN: 978 0 435760 51 9

Edited by Diona Gregory, Ruth Holmes and Sarah Ware
Designed and typeset by Ken Vail Graphic Design

Original illustrations © Harcourt Education Limited 2004

Illustrated by Graham-Cameron Illustration (Ann Biggs), SGA (Mike Lacey), Nick Hawken,
Stuart Harrison, Sylvie Poggio Artists Agency (Rhiannon Powell), John Plumb.

Printed in China by Everbest Printing Company Ltd.

Picture research by Pete Morris

Acknowledgements
The authors and publishers would like to thank the following for permission to use
copyright material.

The publishers have made every effort to trace the copyright holders, but if they have
inadvertently overlooked any, they will be pleased to make the necessary
arrangements at the first opportunity.

For photograph acknowledgements, please see page vii.

Tel: 01865 888058 www.heinemann.co.uk

The author and publishers would like to thank the following for permission to use photographs:

T = top   **B** = bottom   **L** = left   **R** = right   **M** = middle

SPL = Science Photo Library

Cover: Science Photo Library.

Page 2, **T**: Sally and Richard Greenhill; 2, **BL** x2: Getty Images Ltd/PhotoDisc; 2, **BM**: SPL/Jeremy Burgess; 2, **BR**: Holt Studios; 4, **T**: Corbis; 4, **M**: Frank Lane/R Bird; 4, **B**: SPL/BSIP, Fife; 5, **L**: Avoncroft; 5, **R**: Ancient Art and Architecture; 6, **T**: Harcourt Education Ltd/Haddon Davies; 6, **BL**, **BR**: Getty Images Ltd/PhotoDisc; 7, **T**: Harcourt Education Ltd/Peter Morris; 7, **B**: Corbis; 10: SPL/Mark Thomas; 12: SPL/A Glauberman; 16, **L**: John Walmsley; 16, **M**: SPL; 16, **R**: SPL/John Daugherty; 18: Mirrorpix; 20, x2: SPL; 22: Getty Images UK/PhotoDisc; 24, **T**: Getty Images UK/PhotoDisc; 24, **B**: SPL/Adam Hart-Davies; 26, **T**, **M**: Holt Studios/Nigel Cattlin; 26, **B**: Biophoto Associates; 27, x2: Harcourt Education Ltd/Gareth Boden; 28: Holt Studios; 29, **TL**, **TM**, **TR**, **BL**: Harcourt Education Ltd/Peter Morris; 29, **BM**: Corbis; 29, **BR**: Harcourt Education Ltd/Gareth Boden; 31: Environmental Images; 32, **L**, **ML**: Corbis; 32, **MR**, **R**: Getty Images UK/PhotoDisc; 35: SPL/Agstock/Rick Miller; 36: Corbis; 37: Harcourt Education Ltd/Gareth Boden; 38, **T**, **B**: Ecoscene; 38, **M**: Papilio; 42, **T**: Harcourt Education Ltd/Trevor Clifford; 42, **B**: Harcourt Education Ltd/Peter Gould; 43: Harcourt Education Ltd/Gareth Boden; 44, **L**: Alamy; 44, **R**: Harcourt Education Ltd/Peter Gould; 46, **L**, **M**: SPL; 46, **R**: Alamy; 47: Harcourt Education Ltd/Peter Morris; 48, **T**: SPL/Martin Bond; 48, **B**: Harcourt Education Ltd/Andrew Lambert; 49: Harcourt Education Ltd/Haddon Davies; 50: Harcourt Education Ltd/Andrew Lambert; 51, **TL**: Harcourt Education Ltd/Peter Gould; 51, **TR**: Corbis; 51, **BL**: Harcourt Education Ltd/Peter Morris; 51, **BR**: Dorling Kingsley; 52: SPL/Andrew Lambert; 53, **L**: SPL/Andrew Lambert; 53, **R**: Harcourt Education Ltd/Source unknown; 55, x3: Harcourt Education Ltd/Peter Gould; 56: SPL/Jerry Mason; 57, **T**: Harcourt Education Ltd/Peter Gould; 57, **B**: Beken of Cowes; 60: Corbis; 61, **TR**, **ML**, **BR**: Corbis; 61, **BL**: Harcourt Education Ltd/Source unknown; 62: SPL/John Mead; 64, **TL**, **TR**: Corbis RF; 64, **TM**: Getty Images Ltd/PhotoDisc; 64, **B**: Corbis; 66, **T**: Harcourt Education Ltd/Peter Gould; 66, **B**: Getty Images Ltd/PhotoDisc; 67: Getty Images Ltd/PhotoDisc; 68, **TL**, **TR**: Martin Stirrup; 68, **ML**: SPL/Simon Fraser; 68, **MR**, **B**: Getty Images Ltd/PhotoDisc; 69: Alamy; 70: Getty Images Ltd/PhotoDisc; 71, **T**: Rex Features; 71, **B**: Getty Images Ltd/PhotoDisc; 74, **TL**, **BL**: SPL; 74, **TR**: Corbis; 74, **BR**: Getty Images Ltd/PhotoDisc; 75: Harcourt Education Ltd/Peter Morris; 76, x2: Getty Images Ltd/PhotoDisc; 77, **T**: Ecoscene; 77, **B**: Getty Images Ltd/PhotoDisc; 78, x2: Harcourt Education Ltd/Source unknown; 82: Corbis RF; 83: Sherparedside; 84: Harcourt Education Ltd/Chrissie Martin; 86, **TL**: Corbis RF; 86, **TR**: Corbis; 86, **B**: Bubbles/Loisjoy Thurston; 87: Last Resort Picture Library; 88, **T**: Alamy; 88, **ML**: Harcourt Education Ltd/Haddon Davies; 88, **MR**: SPL/Alex Bartel; 88, **B**: Getty Images Ltd/PhotoDisc; 92: Corbis; 93, **T**: SPL/ESA; 93, **B**: NASA; 94, **T**: Ann Ronan; 94, **M**, **B**: SPL; 95, **L**: SPL/Jeremy Burgess; 95, **R**: Mary Evans Picture Library; 96: NASA; 97: NASA; 98: Rex Features; 100, x2: Harcourt Education Ltd/Bea Ray; 101: Harcourt Education Ltd/Peter Gould; 102: Corbis RF; 104: SPL/Keith Kent; 105, **T**, **M**: Corbis RF; 105, **B**: PA Photos; 106, **T**: Mirrorpix; 106, **B**: Alamy; 108, **T**, **B**: Harcourt Education Ltd/Gareth Boden; 108, **M**: Bruce Coleman/Pacific Stock; 110: Robert Harding; 111, **T**: Last Resort Picture Library; 111, **B**: Harcourt Education Ltd/Gareth Boden; 113: Eye Ubiquitous/Corbis/Robert and Linda Mostyn; 115, x2: Harcourt Education Ltd/Gareth Boden; 116: Zefa; 119, **T**, **M**: Getty Images Ltd/PhotoDisc; 119, **BL**, **BR**: Harcourt Education Ltd/Gareth Boden; 128: Harcourt Education Ltd/Andrew Lambert; 129, **T**: Getty Images UK/PhotoDisc; 129, **ML**: Harcourt Education Ltd/Peter Gould; 129, **MR**: Harcourt Education Ltd/Gareth Boden; 129, **B**: Harcourt Education Ltd/Roger Scruton.

A1 The way we are

Why do we look like our parents?

If you look at people in a family you will see that although they are all different, they have many similarities. They have inherited some of the same features from their parents and grandparents.

A baby inherits some features from its mother and some from its father. **Genes** are the instructions for these features. Genes are inside the nucleus of the sperm and the egg.

During fertilisation, the sperm nucleus joins with the egg nucleus to form the first cell of a baby. A baby inherits genes from its father and from its mother. Each baby is unique with its own mix of genes.

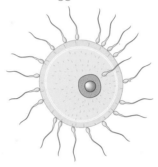

Do you remember?

We call the differences between living things variation. Some variations between the members of a species are inherited and others are caused by their environment.

a Explain what genes do.

James thinks that boys inherit their features from their father and girls inherit their features from their mother.

b Explain to James why his idea is wrong.

Only humans?

Features are inherited in other species too.
Look at the photos below.

c (i) Describe one feature that has been inherited by the rats.
(ii) Describe one feature that has been inherited by the pea plants.

In plants, the pollen grain nucleus and the egg cell nucleus join during fertilisation. The fertilised egg will grow into a new plant. Its features will be controlled by genes inside the pollen grain and the egg cell.

Twins

When a sperm fertilises an egg, the fertilised egg may split into two embryos. Identical twins are formed. Both twins have come from the same sperm and egg, so they have the same genes and the same features.

If there are two separate eggs at the same time, each one may be fertilised by a different sperm. The twins will have different genes and different features. They are non-identical twins.

d What is the difference between identical twins and non-identical twins?

identical twins   non-identical twins

Inherited variation

There are genes to control many of your features.
Your genes decide, for example, whether you will have:

● curly or straight hair

● blue or brown eyes.

e Think about which visible features of your body you may have inherited from each parent. Make a list.

Environmental variation

We also have different features because of our surroundings and choices we make. This is called environmental variation. An example of environmental variation happens if you spend time working out in the gym. Your muscles may get larger, but you make the variation happen. You don't inherit it.

f Think about what features in plants might be affected by the environment. Make a list.

Questions

1 Match each beginning of a sentence with the correct ending. Write down each complete sentence.

Beginnings	Ends
Sperm nucleus and egg nucleus …	… of the sperm and the egg.
We inherit our features …	… one generation to the next.
The information is carried by genes from …	… from our parents.
The genes are in the nucleus …	… join during fertilisation.

2 Draw diagrams and label them to explain how identical and non-identical twins are formed.

3 Two seeds from the same apple were planted in different areas. One tree had large apples, and the other tree had small apples. What do you think caused this variation?

For your notes:

● An organism inherits features from both its parents. These features are controlled by **genes**.

● Identical twins have the same genes because they come from the same sperm and egg.

● Non-identical twins are formed when two sperm fertilise two eggs.

● Both inheritance and the environment cause variation between the members of a species.

A2 Choose your parents

Select a winner

The racehorses in the photo are all members of the same species. Some are taller than others. They have different coloured coats. Some can run faster than others. Racehorse breeders select the fastest runners to breed the next generation of winners!

a Which feature of racehorses are breeders most interested in?

Do you remember?

Members of the same species have similar features. They can reproduce together to continue the species.

Another pint of milk

Mammals such as humans feed their young on their own milk. Cows produce milk to feed their calves after they are born. The amount of milk a cow produces is called the **milk yield**. Farmers are interested in selling milk for a profit, so high milk yield is a **desirable feature** in a cow. This feature can be passed on to the next generation.

High milk yield is a feature that is inherited from both the bull and the cow. Farmers take a bull that can pass on high milk yield and mate it with the cows that produce the most milk. New cattle with higher milk yields may be produced. Farmers select the bull and cows that have the desirable features they want to pass on, and breed from them. This is called **selective breeding**.

b Why is high milk yield a desirable feature?

Selective breeding

Instead of mating a bull and a cow at the farm, scientists at a breeding station may choose a bull that can pass on high milk yield and sell its semen to farmers. The farmer selects a cow with a high milk yield and puts the semen into the cow's vagina through a long tube. We call this **artificial insemination**. The sperm fertilises the cow's egg.

Collecting semen from a bull.

Older breeds

The wild ancestors of our domestic cattle were the aurochs. They are now extinct, but there are cave paintings of them. When a species becomes **extinct**, it dies out altogether and we lose its useful genes.

d How do we know the aurochs ever existed?

Did you know?

To collect the bull's semen, the bull may be introduced to a frame that is made to look like a cow. It has a cow's hide over it and an artificial rubber vagina inside. The bull tries to have sexual intercourse with it, and the semen is collected in the artificial vagina. The semen is frozen until it is needed. The bull never meets a cow!

c What is artificial insemination?

Questions

1 Match each fact with the best reason. Write down each complete sentence.

Fact	Reason
We can breed cattle with high milk yield	so we can use the best bulls to father calves all over the country.
We select the bull and the cow for breeding	because it can be kept until it is needed.
We use artificial insemination	because they can both pass on the high milk yield feature.
We freeze the semen	because it is a feature cows can inherit.

2 Write down the stages of artificial insemination in the correct order.

3 Goldfish come in lots of different colours that look attractive in aquariums. Suggest how more unusual colours might be introduced by selective breeding.

For your notes:

● **Desirable features** are features you want to pass on.

● We can select parents with desirable features to produce new varieties of animals with these same desirable features. This is called **selective breeding**.

5

Sweet and firm?

Think about all the different varieties of tomato that you can buy in a supermarket – different sizes, colours, textures and flavours. Plant breeders have selected different features to produce all of these varieties.

a How many different varieties of tomato can you think of?

A loaf of bread

Wheat is grown to make flour. New modern varieties of wheat have been produced. These have:

- more seeds for making flour
- short stalks to stop them blowing over in the wind
- resistance against disease so they are healthier.

b Look at the two photos on the right. What differences can you see between modern wheat and wild wheat?

Wild wheat.

Modern wheat has been developed from wild wheat by selective breeding.

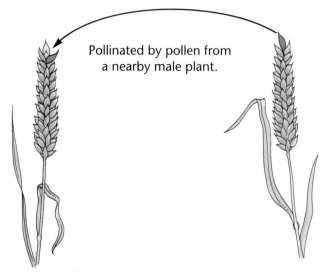

Pollinated by pollen from a nearby male plant.

Female parent treated with chemical to stop production of pollen cells.

male parent

The wheat flower is normally **self-pollinated**. The nucleus of the pollen cell from the male part of the flower fertilises the egg cell of the same flower.

A plant with desirable features can be treated with a special chemical. This stops it producing pollen. Another plant is put nearby that has also been selected for its desirable features. Its pollen pollinates the plant that was treated with the chemical.

Do you remember?

Pollination happens when pollen grains are transferred from an anther to the stigma in a flower.

c How does the farmer make sure that the selected wheat flowers are not self-pollinated?

Research

Moira works in a plant breeding station. She is trying to develop new and better varieties of broccoli to sell to supermarkets.

She has identified these desirable features:

- bright green colour
- large flower heads
- frost resistant
- nice taste
- long shelf-life.

d (i) **Suggest a reason why she has chosen each one of these features.**
(ii) **Which feature do you think is the most important to breed selectively for?**
(iii) **What do you think Moira should do to breed selectively for this feature?**

Feed the world

Scientists have used selective breeding to develop varieties of food crop that can grow in dry conditions and in poor soil. There is a variety of carrot that can grow in very stony ground. This kind of research has helped to provide food in countries where droughts are common.

Did you know?

The Inca Indians in Peru were the first people to cultivate potatoes for food as early as 200 BC. These potatoes looked very different from modern potatoes. They were all different colours – imagine red chips!

Questions

1 Draw a table to show the features of modern wheat and wild wheat. The first row has been done for you.

	Modern wheat	Wild wheat
seeds	more	fewer
stalks		
resistance to disease		

2 Draw a flow chart to show how you can selectively breed wheat.
3 Suggest reasons why it is important to develop new plant varieties.

For your notes:

- Desirable features in plants can be passed on by selective breeding to produce new varieties of plants.

7

Particles 2

Boy or girl?

All the information that decides whether a baby is male or female is carried inside the sperm and the egg. The sperm can have a male Y factor or a female X factor. The egg can only have an X factor.

If an X factor egg is joined by an X factor sperm to give XX, the baby will be a girl. If an X factor egg is joined by a Y factor sperm to give XY, the baby will be a boy.

X Y

ⓐ If a couple's first child is a boy, do you think their second child is more likely to be a girl?

ⓑ Work with a partner. Try spinning a coin 25 times. Write down whether you get heads or tails each time. Count up how many runs of two, three and four you got.

Heads or tails?

If you spin a coin, there are two possible outcomes: heads or tails. There is an equal chance of getting heads or tails. If you get two heads in a row, it is called a run of two. Three heads in a row is called a run of three, and so on.

For every baby that is born, there is an equal chance or **probability** of it being a boy or a girl. The possible combinations of X and Y factors are XX and XY. There are two possibilities, just like spinning a coin. If you have four girls in a row, it is like a run of four heads. The chance of having a girl is always one in two. It doesn't matter how many girls you already have.

Any choice?

The torn and faded pages of a Chinese manuscript tell the story of rich emperor Chan and his wife Jade. Chan desperately wants a son. He is very old fashioned and believes that a son must inherit his wealth. Chan and Jade have five daughters. Chan is hoping for a sixth child – a son. Jade thinks that their family is large enough, and anyway a sixth child might be another girl.

One day, Jade thinks of a plan to change her husband's mind. She makes three types of card.

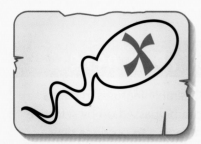

'My dear husband, only you have the power to decide whether our next child will be a boy. Each of your sperm has either the Y factor for a boy or the X factor for a girl. I can only make the X factor.

'There are 10 male cards. 5 have the Y factor and 5 have the X factor. There are 10 female cards. They all have the X factor. I will shuffle the cards. You must choose one male card and one female card each time.

'If you choose:

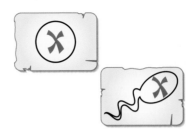

it is the same as having a female child.

'If you choose:

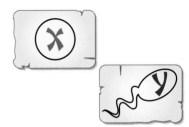

it is the same as having a male child.'

The emperor makes his first choice:

c **What is the sex of this 'child'?**

The emperor puts back the cards. He makes four more choices, and each time the combination is female. 'Fascinating! This is just like our family!' Chan exclaims in surprise.

d **Do you think this result is surprising? Explain your answer.**

The bargain

'Now you must make your sixth choice,' said Jade. 'If your sixth choice is male, I will agree to having another baby, but if your sixth choice is female, our family is complete and all our wealth will be divided between our five daughters.'

e What do you think is the probability of the sixth choice being male?

f Do you think Jade's card game was a good idea? Explain your reasons.

Questions

1 Discuss the beginnings and ends of sentences below with a partner. Match each beginning of a sentence with the correct ending. Write down each complete sentence.

Beginnings	Ends
Half of a man's sperm will have …	… the X factor.
All of a woman's eggs will have …	… both the X and Y factors.
None of the man's sperm will have …	… the Y factor.

2 The Smith family have three children. The oldest one is a boy and the two younger girls are twins. What do you think is the probability of their fourth child being a boy?

B1 Are you fit?

Fit and healthy

What is fitness?

Fitness means different things to different people.

a Which of these people do you think are fit?

If you are fit, your body is good at providing glucose and oxygen to your cells for respiration. It is also good at getting rid of the carbon dioxide and water from respiration.

Do you remember?

Respiration happens when glucose and oxygen react in your cells to release energy.

oxygen + glucose → carbon dioxide + water | **energy is released**

Keeping your cells going

When you exercise, your muscle cells respire more to release more energy. To do this, they need more oxygen and glucose. They need to get rid of more carbon dioxide and water. Your organ systems help to make this happen.

● Your digestive system breaks down the nutrients in food into small molecules like glucose. Glucose goes into the blood and is carried to your cells.

● Oxygen enters your body and carbon dioxide leaves your body through your breathing or **respiratory system**. If you breathe faster, you take in oxygen and get rid of carbon dioxide more quickly.

● Blood carries substances around your body in the **circulatory system**. **Red blood cells** carry the oxygen needed for respiration. If your heart beats faster, it pumps the blood to your cells more quickly. This means your cells can respire more quickly to release more energy. You can measure how fast your heart is beating by taking your pulse, like the doctor in the photo.

b Which three organ systems work together to supply your cells with glucose and oxygen?

Do you remember?

A balanced diet contains the correct amounts of nutrients (carbohydrate, fat, protein, vitamins and minerals), along with fibre and water. Deficiencies of nutrients make people ill.

Red blood cell.

Did you know?

You know that the organs for digestion make up the digestive system. In the same way, the organs for breathing are called the respiratory system. The organs for moving blood around the body are called the circulatory system.

c Look at this graph. Why do you think the breathing rate is low between midnight and 6 am?

d This man is a gardener. Why does his breathing rate go up when he gets to work?

Why are some people so fit?

Look at James and Aisha after a run.

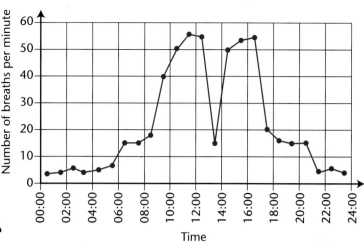

e Whose heart do you think is beating faster, and who is breathing faster?

f Who do you think is fitter?

Aisha is fitter than James. She exercises regularly. Regular exercise helps your heart and lungs work better.

- Her lungs take in more oxygen in every breath. Aisha didn't need to breathe as fast as James during the run to get enough oxygen into her blood.

- A stronger heart pumps more blood around the body with every beat. Aisha's heart didn't need to beat as fast as James's to supply her muscle cells with oxygen.

So if I want to be fit, I need to exercise more?

Yes. Exercise keeps your heart, lungs, muscles and joints working properly. It prevents heart disease and improves the blood circulation. To keep fit you also need to eat a balanced diet, and avoid smoking and alcohol.

Questions

1 Match each beginning with the correct ending. Write down each complete sentence.

Beginnings	Ends
Your fitness can be affected by …	… glucose and oxygen react together.
A balanced diet contains …	… energy.
Respiration happens when …	… the correct amounts of nutrients to stay healthy.
Respiration releases …	… the amount of exercise you get.

2 Which organ systems provide your cells with:

a glucose?   **b** oxygen?

3 Explain why fitter people have slower heartbeats and breathe more slowly.

For your notes:

- **Fit** people can get enough oxygen and glucose to their cells for respiration, even when they are exercising.

- To keep fit, your digestive system, your **respiratory system** and your **circulatory system** need to be working properly.

Breathing and smoking

How do we breathe?

You breathe to take oxygen into your body for respiration, and to get rid of carbon dioxide made by respiration. Put your hands on your chest, and feel your ribcage. It is wrapped around your lungs.

a Take a deep breath in and out. How does the ribcage move when you breathe in and out?

Look at the diagram below to see what happens when you breathe.

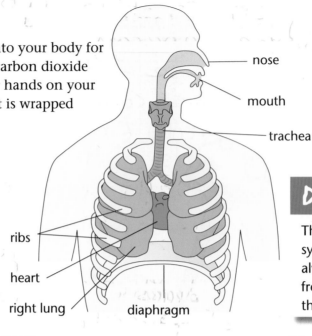

nose

mouth

trachea

ribs

heart

right lung

diaphragm

Do you remember?

The insides of your respiratory system contain millions of tiny alveoli (air sacs). Oxygen moves from the air in the alveoli into the blood.

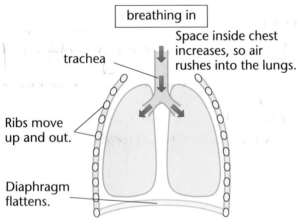

breathing in

Space inside chest increases, so air rushes into the lungs.

trachea

Ribs move up and out.

Diaphragm flattens.

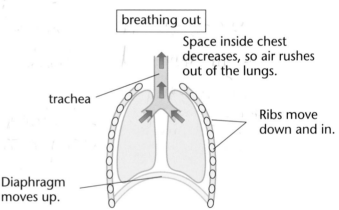

breathing out

Space inside chest decreases, so air rushes out of the lungs.

trachea

Ribs move down and in.

Diaphragm moves up.

Understanding a cigarette packet

If you smoke, you breathe in a lot of harmful chemicals. These damage the alveoli in your lungs. This means you take in less oxygen each time you breathe in.

Your body's cells can't respire as much, so they release less energy and you feel tired. Many smokers get out of breath quickly because they are breathing more often to get enough oxygen.

You can see how smoking has damaged the lung on the left compared with a normal lung (far left).

Cigarette packets warn smokers about the effects of smoking.

Stopping smoking reduces the risk of fatal heart and lung diseases

Tar causes lung cancer and bronchitis. It clogs up the tiny alveoli, so it's harder for oxygen to get into the blood.

Poisonous carbon monoxide in cigarette smoke reduces the amount of oxygen your blood can carry.

Smoking kills

Smoking causes fatal lung cancer

Lung cancer is a ball of cells that uses up space in your lungs. This leaves less space for air, and less oxygen gets into your blood.

If you breathe in someone else's smoke, you could have the same health problems as someone who actually smokes.

Smoking seriously harms you and others around you

Smoking is highly addictive

Nicotine makes it hard to give up smoking. It can give you high blood pressure and heart disease.

Smoking when pregnant harms your baby

Smoking reduces the oxygen supply to the baby's cells. This stops the baby developing properly.

Smoking can cause a slow and painful death

Inside your trachea, mucus traps dirt and bacteria. Smokers cough to try to get rid of this mucus.

Smoking clogs the arteries and causes heart attacks and strokes

Questions

1 Copy and complete the sentences by choosing from the words in bold.

   a Passive smoking happens when you **breathe in/breathe out** smoke from someone else.

   b When you breathe out, your ribs go **up and out/down and in**.

   c When you breathe in, the space inside your chest gets **larger/smaller**.

   d The air you breathe in contains **more/less** oxygen than the air you breathe out.

2 a Write down the parts of the respiratory system that carbon dioxide travels through on its way from the alveoli to the mouth.

   b How do the ribs move to help push air out of the lungs?

3 Explain how these chemicals can affect your health:

   a nicotine   b tar.

For your notes:

- When you breathe in, the space in your chest increases and air rushes in. When you breathe out, the space in your chest decreases and air rushes out.

- Cigarette smoke contains chemicals that reduce the amount of oxygen reaching your cells.

B3 Drugs and alcohol

What is a drug?

These people like taking drugs. A **drug** is a substance that changes how your body works, or how you think and feel.

● Edward takes caffeine, Jill takes alcohol and Hassan takes nicotine. These are **recreational drugs**. They take them often and it's legal to take them.

● Joanna is taking antibiotics for a week. These are **medical drugs**. The doctor has given them to her because she is ill.

● Some people take **illegal drugs**. They harm the body and may cause death.

a Write down one difference between medical drugs and illegal drugs.

All drugs have **side effects**. These are not the main effects of the drug, like curing your illness. They are other effects that happen as well, such as feeling sleepy or sick. Side effects may damage your organs. If you take too many drugs, the side effects can make you very ill or even kill you.

Many drugs are **addictive**. When a drug's effects have worn off, people feel bad and need more of it to feel good again. Caffeine, nicotine and alcohol make people feel they need a coffee, a cigarette or a glass of beer or wine. Some medical and illegal drugs can be just as addictive.

Drugs close up

Andrew is a social worker who works with people who are addicted to illegal drugs. He carries information cards to help him work out which drugs people have been taking.

b Which type of drug seems to have the most harmful side effects?

Heroin

Why do people take it?

Makes you feel happy even if things are bad

Side effects

Feeling sick, vomiting, very addictive and can lead to unconciousness, coma or even death

AIDs from infected needles

Cannabis

Why do people take it?

Makes you feel relaxed

Side effects

May make you feel confused and disorientated

Infertility in men

Poor coordination

Bronchitis and lung cancer

Cocaine

Why do people take it?

Makes you alert and confident

Speeds up your body's reactions

Side effects

May cause depression and thoughts that everyone is against you

Constipation

Extreme nervousness

Dangerous for people with heart problems

Alcohol

Steph is drunk. She is suffering from the side effects of alcohol. Look what her friends are saying about her.

She can't see where she's going.

Her speech is so slurred it's hard to understand her.

She's very sleepy.

She's about to lose her balance.

She's been to the toilet five times in the last hour!

Stop her driving home! Her reactions aren't quick enough to drive.

She's very confident now but she's usually so shy.

C **Write down a list of ways in which alcohol can affect people.**

Alcohol, like many drugs, can have long-term side effects. It can damage the liver and brain, and cause cancer. If Steph ever gets pregnant, she should stop drinking alcohol. It can prevent her baby developing properly.

Did you know?

Alcohol is measured in **units of alcohol**. All of the drinks in this picture contain one unit of alcohol. It is illegal to drive after drinking more than two or three units: the amount depends on your size.

 or or

$\frac{1}{2}$ pint of beer or lager | single measure of spirits | small glass of wine | = 1 unit of alcohol

Questions

1 Copy and complete the sentences by choosing from the words in bold.

  a Cocaine makes people more **alert/sleepy**.

  b Heroin and cannabis are **legal/illegal** drugs.

  c It is dangerous to drive after drinking alcohol because it **slows down/speeds up** people's body reactions.

  d Side effects are what people **want/don't want** from the drug.

2 What is a drug?

3 Write down one example of:

  a a recreational drug   **b** a medical drug   **c** an illegal drug.

4 Explain what 'addictive' means.

For your notes:

- A **drug** is a substance that changes how your body works, or alters the way you think and feel.

- Many drugs are **addictive** and have different short-term and long-term **side effects** on your body.

Learn about:
- Bones and joints
- Injuries to bones and joints

Broken bones

Anna broke her leg while playing football. She was carried off the pitch and rushed to hospital. The doctor has set her leg in plaster so the broken pieces can grow back together again. You can see her X-ray below.

The **skeleton** has many bones which keep Anna upright and help her move around. A broken leg can't support Anna, so a plaster cast gives support until the bone mends.

Parts of the skeleton also protect delicate organs. The ribs protect the lungs. Look back at page 12 to see this.

a Which part of the skeleton would protect Anna's brain when she heads a ball?

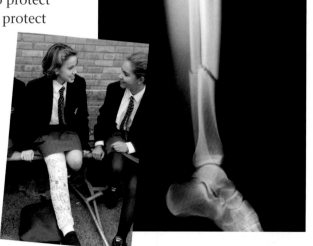

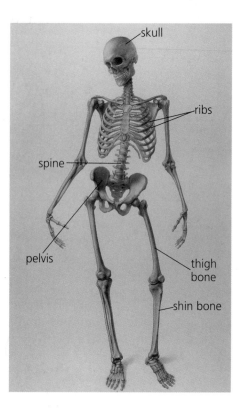

Movement and joints

Wiggle the tip of your little finger backwards and forwards. If your finger were made of just one bone, it would be impossible to wiggle it. There are **joints** in your skeleton. Joints allow your bones to move.

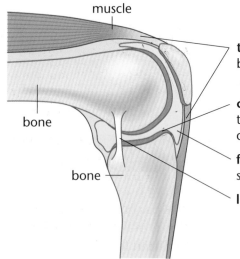

Hinge joint (knee).

tendon – connects the muscle to the bone

cartilage – smooth tissue which helps the ends of the bones slide over each other

fluid – acts like oil, helping the bones slide over each other

ligament – holds the bones together

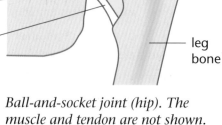

Ball-and-socket joint (hip). The muscle and tendon are not shown.

b What holds the bones together in a joint?

c Name two things that help the bones slide over each other.

Different types of joint let your bones move in different ways:

- The knee joint is a hinge joint. The bone can only move backwards and forwards.

- Ball-and-socket joints let the bone move in all directions. Good examples are your shoulders and hips. There is a ball at the end of your upper arm and leg bones. This rotates inside the socket in the shoulder and hip bone.

When joints go wrong

Athletes work hard and put their bodies under lots of stress, so they often damage their joints. Marc is a physiotherapist working with Anna's football team. He treats injured people. The goalkeeper has collapsed in pain, and the referee has called Marc onto the pitch.

I think you may have torn the cartilage in your knee joint. You'll need an operation to remove any loose bits of cartilage.

My knee has been hurting for weeks. I think the cartilage has probably been wearing away for quite a while.

Damaged cartilage isn't the only problem you can get with joints. If you don't warm up properly, or if you make sudden movements, you can also stretch your ligaments. This is what happens when you get a **sprain**.

Questions

1. Write out each part of the body along with its correct function.

Body parts	Functions
knee joint	holds the bones together
cartilage	keeps us upright and helps us move
ligament	helps the bones slide across each other
skeleton	lets the lower leg move backwards and forwards

2. Explain the job of:

   a the fluid

   b the ligaments in the knee joint.

3. Write down two ways in which joints can be damaged.

For your notes:

- The **skeleton** helps you stay upright, helps you move, and protects important organs.

- Bones can be moved at **joints** and are held together by **ligaments**.

- Joints contain **cartilage** and **fluid** which helps the bones slide across each other.

- Injuries can happen to bones and joints. You can break bones, and **sprain** or stretch ligaments.

Muscles and tendons

Alex never warms up before exercise. Unfortunately, he's torn his Achilles tendon and can't walk. Tendons are special fibres that join muscles to bones.

a Put your hand on the front of your upper arm, and bend your elbow. What happens to the front muscle of your upper arm?

Your front upper arm muscle **contracts** – it gets shorter and fatter. When the muscle contracts it pulls a tendon, which pulls the bones in your lower arm upwards.

b Now straighten your arm. What happens to the front and back muscles of your upper arm?

Your front upper arm muscle **relaxes** – it gets longer and thinner. Your back upper arm muscle contracts. A relaxed muscle can't pull or push anything, so muscles have to work in pairs to pull bones backwards and forwards. When one muscle contracts, the other relaxes.

A tendon links the front muscle to the lower arm bones. If this is torn, you cannot bend your arm any more. It is also very painful! The same thing happened when Alex tore his Achilles tendon. He can't bend and straighten his ankle any more.

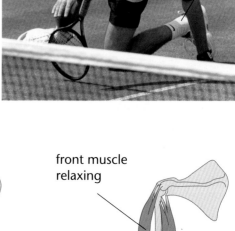

Achilles tendon

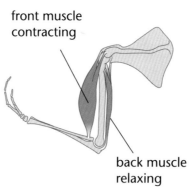

front muscle contracting

back muscle relaxing

Raising the arm.

front muscle relaxing

back muscle contracting

Lowering the arm.

Fitness programmes

All parts of our bodies need to work well together to keep us fit. Janet is a fitness instructor. She has written a fitness programme for Ivor.

I ♥ PIES

Fitness programme
No fatty foods
Stop smoking
One pint of beer each week
20-minute fast walk each day

You must keep your heart healthy to pump blood around your body.

If you eat too much fat, or drink too much alcohol, the blood vessels leading to your heart may get blocked. This could give you heart disease.

Smoking increases your blood pressure, and makes your heart beat faster. This can wear out your heart.

c Why has Janet banned Ivor from eating fish and chips?

This is Janet's fitness programme for Mary, who wants to train for a marathon.

Fitness programme

Continue to eat healthily

Swim 2 km two mornings each week

Run 5 km three evenings each week

Go for a very long run every weekend

Regular exercise makes your heart grow stronger, so that each heartbeat pumps more blood to your muscles.

Regular exercise increases the number of blood vessels carrying blood to your muscle cells, helping them to respire more.

d **Who do you think was fitter before they started their fitness programme, Ivor or Mary?**

Janet always recommends doing a warm-up before beginning any physical exercise. It is easy to hurt your muscles and joints when exercising. You may sprain a ligament or **strain** (pull) a muscle if you do not warm up properly.

Questions

1 Write out each term on the left along with its correct description.

Terms	Descriptions
muscle contracts	what you need to do to make your heart and lungs stronger
fitness programme	hurt muscle
regular exercise	muscle gets shorter and fatter, pulling on a bone
strain	instructions on what to eat and how to exercise

2 Explain:

a why you should not eat too much fat

b why you should warm up carefully.

3 Explain how regular exercise makes you fitter.

4 Design a leaflet to explain to Year 7 pupils about the importance of a healthy lifestyle.

For your notes:

- Muscles are joined to bones by tendons. Both can be injured if you do not warm up properly.

- Muscles work in pairs. They **contract** and **relax**. They can pull bones, but cannot push them.

- To keep fit, you need to eat healthily, exercise regularly, and cut down on smoking and drinking.

B6 Working together

Faulty joints

I've got arthritis in my hip joint. The cartilage has worn away and my doctor has offered me a replacement hip joint.

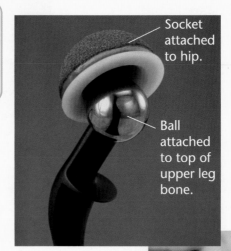

Socket attached to hip.

Ball attached to top of upper leg bone.

You can see an artificial hip joint in these photos. An artificial hip joint will get Reg active again and free of pain. But like his natural hip joint, the artificial one will wear out too. Artificial hip joints often need replacing.

a **Make a list of properties that an artificial joint needs to have. Look back to page 16 if you need help.**

Using evidence

Terry runs a lab that works on artificial joints. He wants his team to design an artificial hip joint to last a lifetime. He knows that to make a really good joint, he'll need help from scientists who discover and develop new materials (materials scientists). He'll also need expert advice from surgeons and physiotherapists who work with patients.

When scientists work together like this they often have better ideas than when they work on their own. Terry decided to have a meeting to look at how to improve the design of artificial hip joints.

I help people to walk again after they have a new joint fitted. The ball and socket of artificial joints often rub together. This makes it difficult to walk.

Artificial joints often wear away. The ball and socket rub together, scraping off thousands of tiny bits. These bits damage people's bones.

Artificial joints often work loose from the hip bone.

surgeon

physiotherapist

materials scientist

b **If you were Terry, what would you do to improve artificial hip joints?**

Terry decided to work on improving the way the socket is attached to the hip bone, and the material the ball and socket are made from.

Testing cement

Terry found out that joints are fixed to the bone in two ways:

- using cement
- making the hole in the hip bone the same shape and size as the artificial socket, so the socket just slots in. After a few weeks, the hip bone grows into the artificial socket, holding it in place.

Terry asked the surgeon to find information about the failure of replacement joints.

c Look at the table on the right. Younger people's bones grow more quickly than older people's bones. Why were 'no cement' joints in young people more successful than in older people?

Age group	Type of fixing	Percentage of joints that failed within 10 years
20–39	cement	25
	no cement	8
40–59	cement	16
	no cement	17
60–79	cement	8
	no cement	25

Trialing materials

Terry decided to do some research to find out which materials to make hip joints from. He asked the materials scientist to run some trials using three different materials and a simulator. This moved the ball backwards and forwards in the socket all the time. He tested 50 of each joint. The results are shown in the table below.

d Which materials would you choose for the socket and for the ball?

e Think about what you did at lunchtime. Write down how many minutes you spent walking, running and standing still.

f Think about your answer to question d. Does Terry's simulator put his artificial joints through the same stresses and strains as your hip goes through each day?

Socket	Ball	Amount of joint worn away in a year, in mm³
polyethylene	metal	2.8
metal	metal	0.8
ceramic	ceramic	0.004

Questions

Terry asked for permission to run trials with humans. The physiotherapist is going to use 200 patients across the country.

1 Why will Terry get a better idea of how good the joint is by trialling it with humans than with a simulator?

2 Explain why Terry is going to use 200 patients rather than just one patient.

3 Terry finalised his new hip joint design. What materials and fixing method should he tell a surgeon to use for:

a an 18-year-old patient?

b an 80-year-old patient?

4 Look back through these two pages. Write a flow chart showing what you think each scientist did, and the order in which they did it.

C1 Hungry plants

Where do plants get food?

Plants need food to respire and grow, but how do they get this food?

a Which of these people below do you agree with?

I think that plants take in all their food through their roots.

I think that plants make their own food using energy from the Sun.

I think plants make their own food from carbon dioxide and water.

Matthew   Andrew   Jenny

In fact, both Andrew and Jenny are correct. Plants make their food in their leaves from carbon dioxide and water using energy from the Sun. This process is called **photosynthesis**.

How does photosynthesis work?

In photosynthesis, plants change carbon dioxide and water into oxygen and a sugar called glucose. They use the sugar for food. The change needs light energy from the Sun. Photosynthesis happens mainly in the leaves.

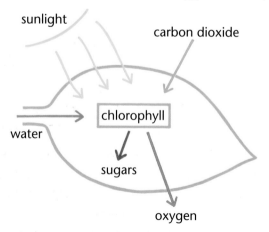

sunlight

carbon dioxide

chlorophyll

water

sugars

oxygen

Jenny drew a diagram to show exactly what happens in photosynthesis, and wrote out the word equation.

carbon dioxide + water $\xrightarrow{\text{light energy}}$ glucose + oxygen

b What are the: (i) reactants and (ii) products in photosynthesis?

How does light affect plants?

In Jessica's house there is a plant in every room. She thinks it makes the house look nice, but she can't work out why the plant in the living room grows so much more quickly than the plant in the hallway. You can see the two plants in this picture.

Using what you know about photosynthesis, answer these questions for Jessica.

c Which room gets more light, the living room or the hallway?

d Which plant can photosynthesise more quickly? Explain why.

Questions

1 Copy and complete these sentences by choosing from the words in bold.

  a Plants make food by a process called **photosynthesis/respiration**.

  b Plants get **light/electrical** energy from the Sun.

  c Most photosynthesis happens in the **roots/leaves**.

  d Photosynthesis produces sugar and **carbon dioxide/oxygen**.

2 What would happen to photosynthesis if a plant was kept:

  a in the dark for a few days?   **b** without any carbon dioxide?

3 Look back at the products of photosynthesis. Suggest one reason why humans would not survive without plants.

For your notes:

- Plants make food by a process called **photosynthesis**. This happens mainly in the leaves.

- In photosynthesis, plants take in carbon dioxide and water and use light energy to make oxygen and glucose.

Catching the Sun

Look at this photo of a house. It's very 'eco-friendly'. It makes its own electricity using solar cells on the roof.

a **When light hits the solar cell, it makes electricity. Why are solar cells broad, flat and thin?**

The solar cell takes in a lot of light because it is broad and flat.

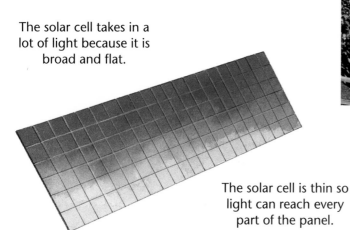

The solar cell is thin so light can reach every part of the panel.

Looking at a leaf

A **leaf** is a plant organ that is similar to a solar cell. Photosynthesis happens in chloroplasts, which are inside some plant cells. Leaf cells have lots of chloroplasts. Chloroplasts contain **chlorophyll**, which is green. Chlorophyll takes in the light energy from the Sun.

Look at this picture of the leaves.

b **Why do you think leaves are broad and flat like the solar cell?**

c **Why do you think leaves are thin like solar cells?**

To photosynthesise easily, leaves need to be able to:

● take in carbon dioxide

● get water

● take in light energy.

Looking close up

We can slice a leaf open, and have a look at the cells inside it using a microscope. This will help us see how leaves are adapted to photosynthesise well.

ⓓ The stomata let carbon dioxide into the leaf. Which gas produced by photosynthesis would escape through the stomata?

ⓔ Most of the chloroplasts are in the palisade cells near the top surface of the leaf. How does this help the plant?

In any living thing, different cells have different jobs. To help them do their job properly, they have special features. Palisade cells have special features to help them photosynthesise:

● They have lots of chloroplasts, which contain chlorophyll. Chlorophyll takes in light energy, and so cells with lots of chlorophyll can photosynthesise a lot.

● They are long and thin. This means lots of palisade cells are packed tightly together, making sure that they catch as much light energy as possible.

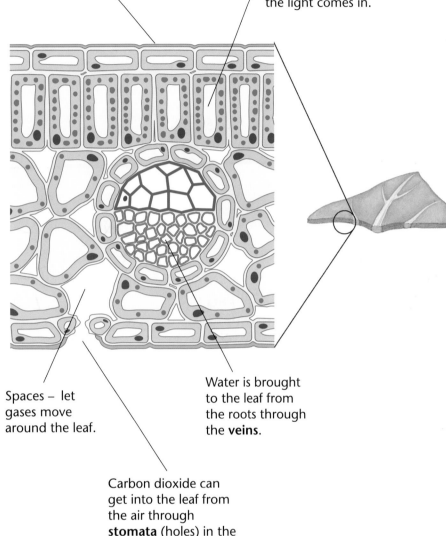

Plants can lose water through their leaves but the waxy, waterproof layer stops water loss from the top surface.

Light can get to the chloroplasts easily. Most of the chloroplasts are in the palisade layer of cells, near to the top of the leaf where the light comes in.

Spaces – let gases move around the leaf.

Water is brought to the leaf from the roots through the **veins**.

Carbon dioxide can get into the leaf from the air through **stomata** (holes) in the underside of the leaf.

Questions

1 Copy and complete these sentences using the words below.

     water   chloroplasts   gases   light energy

Photosynthesis happens in the _____ in the leaf. Leaves are broad and flat to take in a lot of _____. Leaves have holes in to let _____ in and out. Leaves have a waxy top surface to stop _____ being lost.

2 **a** What do the palisade cells have a lot of to help with photosynthesis?

  b Palisade cells are long and thin. How does this help the plant?

3 Describe how carbon dioxide gets from the air to the palisade cells, and how oxygen gets from the palisade cells to the air.

For your notes:

● **Leaves** are broad and flat to catch as much sunlight as possible.

● Leaves have **veins** to transport water, and **stomata** to let carbon dioxide and oxygen in and out.

● Some cells have special features to carry out particular jobs.

Why water?

Jamal's in trouble. His parents have got back from holiday, and their plants have drooped. Jamal was supposed to have watered them every day, but he didn't think it was important and he forgot.

> *Don't you realise that plants need water for photosynthesis?*

> *And you were supposed to put fertiliser in the water to give the plants nutrients to keep them healthy.*

a What do plants use water for?

b Why do plants need nutrients?

What do roots do?

Roots are plant organs that grow deep and spread out in the soil to reach water. They have two main jobs:

- They take in water and nutrients from the soil.
- They hold the plant firm in the soil.

Roots get thinner and thinner as they spread out. The very tips of roots have many tiny parts called **root hairs**.

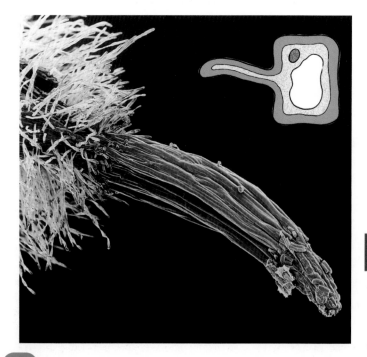

Root hairs are long and thin parts of the root hair cell, sticking out into the soil. They increase the surface of the roots in contact with water in the soil. This means the roots can take in water more quickly. There are nutrients dissolved in the water in the soil, and the roots take in these nutrients along with the water.

To increase the supply of nutrients, some gardeners also add **fertiliser** to the water. Fertiliser contains dissolved nutrients, which help to keep plants healthy.

Did you know?

Even root cells need oxygen from the air for respiration. If you give a plant too much water, it stops oxygen in the air getting to the roots, and the plant will die.

Reaching all parts

Once in the roots, water is carried up through the stem and into the leaves and flowers by tubes called veins. If you stand a plant in red dye, you can see the movement of water through the veins. If you cut a slice out of the stem, the red dye shows up in the veins. The celery stem in these photos shows this.

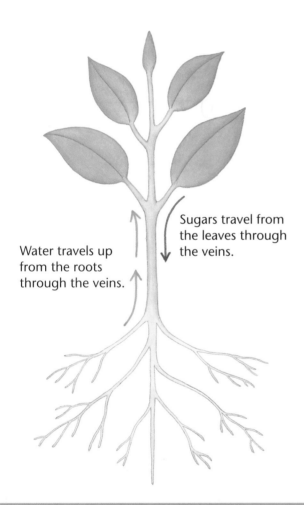

Sugars travel from the leaves through the veins.

Water travels up from the roots through the veins.

All cells need water

Veins carry water and nutrients up the plant stem to the leaves, where the water is used for photosynthesis to make food. Water also helps the food travel around the plant to all its cells. The food dissolves in water and is carried through the veins to other parts of the plant so the plant's cells can use it.

Plants need water to stay upright. If you don't water a plant, it wilts and goes floppy. To stay upright, a plant's cells need to be full of water. This is why it is important that water gets to all the cells in a plant.

Did you know?

Some parts of a plant are almost all water. A ripe tomato is about 95% water.

Questions

1 Maria has just watered the tomatoes in her greenhouse. She added fertiliser to the water before watering her cucumbers.

  a Write down two reasons why plants need water.

  b How will the fertiliser help the cucumbers grow?

2 Maria poured the water onto the soil so that it would soak in and reach the roots quickly.

  a Write down two jobs of the roots.

  b What do roots have that makes them good at absorbing water and nutrients?

3 Write a story about the journey of a water droplet from the soil into the plant and up to the leaves.

For your notes:

● Plants need water and nutrients to stay healthy.

● **Roots** take in water and nutrients, and hold a plant firm in the ground.

● **Root hairs** have a large surface area to help roots to take in a lot of water and nutrients.

● Veins carry water and nutrients to all parts of the plant.

Biopower

Look at this advertisement for the new electricity company BioPower. This company makes electricity by burning renewable plant material such as wood and straw.

Do you realise that burning coal is polluting your environment?

Do you want to make electricity without burning coal?

Do you want to be environmentally friendly?

Then welcome to BioPower, the only electricity company to generate electricity by burning biomass.

BioPower

Plant biomass is a renewable energy resource and burning it makes less pollution than burning coal or oil.

Did you know?

Biomass is plant and animal material. It is a store of chemical energy. We measure biomass by finding the total mass of the animal or plant material, not including its water.

a What do BioPower power stations burn to generate electricity?

b Where does the energy in biomass come from?

Biomass

Photosynthesis makes glucose. Some of the glucose is used by the plant in respiration, to release energy. Most of the glucose is used for growth. It is changed into materials for new cells, new leaves, and new stems. All this new plant material is biomass.

Look at this picture of vegetables on a market stall to see where biomass can be stored in a plant. Many of these plant organs store glucose as starch.

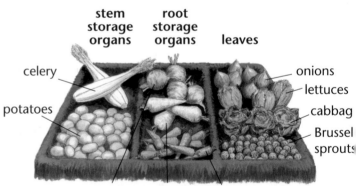

stem storage organs · root storage organs · leaves

celery · onions · lettuces · cabbage · Brussel sprouts

potatoes · turnips · parsnips · carrots

Plants store starch in roots, stems and leaves to help them survive into the next year. If we did not pull up carrots and eat them, they would use the energy in the stored starch to grow again in the spring. Plants also store biomass in fruit and seeds to help their seedlings grow and develop in the spring.

The carrot flower stores biomass in its seeds, ready to make new plants next year.

Using plant biomass

Look at these pictures showing how we use plant biomass.
We use all parts of a plant – leaves, stems, flowers, seeds and roots.

Corn oil is made from corn plants. It contains fat.

Golden syrup is made from sugar cane. It contains sucrose.

Textured vegetable protein (TVP) comes from vegetables. Vegetarians can eat TVP to give them protein.

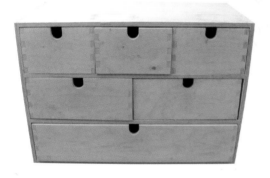

Wooden furniture and wooden houses are made from trees, and cotton jeans are made from cotton plants. All of these contain cellulose.

c **Write down as many ways as you can in which humans use plant biomass.**

Questions

1 Match each beginning of a sentence with the correct endings. Write down each complete sentence.

Beginnings	Endings
The total mass of a living thing, not …	… is made from glucose.
Starch …	… the roots, stem or leaves.
Biomass can be stored in …	… makes other substances.
Photosynthesis makes glucose which …	… including water, is called the biomass.

2 Write down some ways in which plants use the biomass they make from glucose.

3 Write down four ways in which the biomass of plants is used in your home.

For your notes:

- Biomass is the total mass of plant or animal material, not including water.

- Glucose can be converted into starch and stored.

- Humans use plant biomass in lots of different ways.

Spot the difference

Learn about:
- Respiration and photosynthesis
- Green plants and the environment

Making food and getting energy

Fatima's younger brother Joe was asking her how plants eat. Fatima explained how plants photosynthesise to make their own food. She wrote down the word equation on the right for photosynthesis.

Photosynthesis

$$\text{carbon dioxide + water} \xrightarrow[\text{chlorophyll}]{\text{light energy}} \text{glucose + oxygen}$$

Fatima remembered that animals break down their food to get energy in respiration, and plants do the same thing. Plants respire to get the energy from the food they have made. She wrote down the word equation on the right for respiration.

$$\text{glucose + oxygen} \xrightarrow{\text{energy released}} \text{carbon dioxide + water}$$

She noticed that both equations had the same substances in them.

ⓐ Look at the two equations. What can you say about the reactants in photosynthesis and the products in respiration?

Day and night

Plants need energy all day and all night to stay alive so they respire all the time. Plants can only photosynthesise during the day when there is enough sunlight.

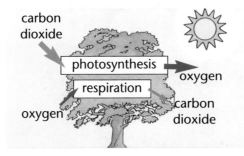
Photosynthesis is faster than respiration during the day.

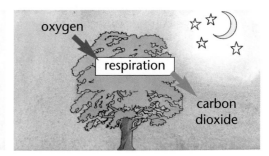
Only respiration takes place at night.

ⓑ Where does:
(i) respiration
(ii) photosynthesis happen in a plant?

ⓒ Which gas do plants make both during the day and during the night?

ⓓ Which gas do plants make only during the day?

Why are rainforests important?

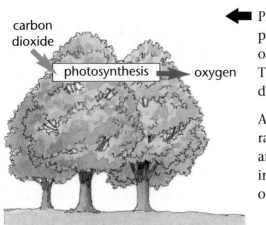

Plants in the rainforest photosynthesise and put oxygen into the air. They take out carbon dioxide from the air.

All organisms, including rainforest plants, respire and put carbon dioxide into the air. They take out oxygen from the air.

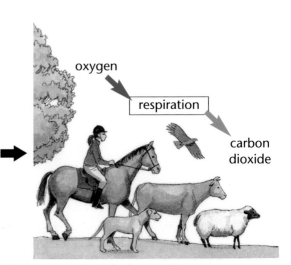

When photosynthesis by plants and respiration by plants and animals are in balance, the levels of carbon dioxide and oxygen stay the same.

The rainforests cover huge areas of Africa, Asia and South America. Large areas of rainforest are being cut down and burned. Sometimes the forests are cleared so that the wood can be used for making paper, furniture or building materials. Sometimes the forests are just burned so the ground can be used for farming. People grow crops there which they can sell. People are very worried because they think carbon dioxide levels in the atmosphere will go up, and oxygen levels will go down. We all need oxygen for respiration. More carbon dioxide in the air could make global warming worse.

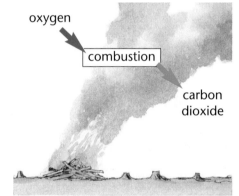

e Why may carbon dioxide levels in the air go up if the rainforests are cut down?

f Why is it a problem if oxygen levels in the air go down?

Questions

1 Copy and complete these sentences using the words below.

   photosynthesis   **every cell**   **go up**   **during**

   a Respiration happens in _____ of every animal and plant.

   b Cutting down rainforests may make carbon dioxide levels _____ in the air around the world.

   c _____ happens in plants during the day when it is light.

   d Respiration happens _____ the night and the day.

2 Copy this table and complete it using ticks and crosses to show which gases a plant gives out and takes in. The first row has been done for you.

	Day	Night
gives out carbon dioxide	✓	✓
takes in carbon dioxide		
gives out oxygen		
takes in oxygen		

3 Plants are often taken out of hospital wards at night. Suggest a reason for this.

For your notes:

- Plants release energy from food by respiration, just like animals. Respiration takes place in every cell of a plant.

- Cutting down rainforests may increase carbon dioxide levels in the air around the Earth.

31

Learn about:
● Food stores in plants
● Humans in a food web

D1 Storing food

Best in show!

Marcus has entered a vegetable show. The rules are simple: the vegetable with the biggest biomass wins!

a Look back at Unit C Plants and photosynthesis. What is biomass?

Do you remember?

Plants make glucose by photosynthesis. Some glucose is stored as starch or changed into other materials so the plants grow. Biomass is all the materials in plants except water.

b Look at the pictures below showing food stores in plants. Which part of each plant is the food store that humans eat?

   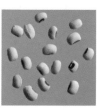

root   stem   fruit   seed

Why store food?

It's tempting to think that plants store food for us to eat. But they really do it for the same reasons as people save money.

In the summer there's lots of light. Plants can make more food than they need, so they store some. In the winter, when they need glucose for respiration, they can use the stored food.

We save any spare money in the bank ready for when we need it.

In autumn plants store food in their seeds, so the tiny plant inside has food when it starts to grow in spring.

We save money to bring up children.

We save money in the bank to keep it safe from robbers.

Some plants like rhubarb store food in their stems, and surround the stem with poisonous leaves to stop animals eating them.

Humans in a food web

Look at the meal on the table. The different foods in the meal come from either animals or plants. Humans eat lots of different animals and plants, so they are in lots of different food chains. Here are some of the food chains involved in this meal:

carrot → human	grass → cow → human
broccoli → human	potato → human

If you put food chains together, you can make a food web. You can see a food web in the diagram on the right.

Animals can't make food themselves. They must eat other living things to get food for energy. They are consumers. When a consumer eats another living thing, the energy stored in its biomass is passed on. The arrows show the energy transfer.

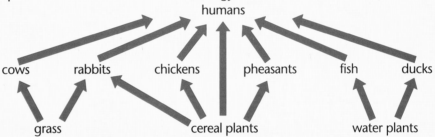

There are several different types of consumer – omnivores, carnivores and herbivores.

Plants make food themselves using light energy from the Sun. The Sun is the energy source for the food web. Plants are producers.

Do you remember?

Energy enters food chains and food webs when producers photosynthesise using light energy from the Sun.

Questions

1 Match the words below to their definitions. Write out each word with its correct definition.

Words	Definitions
food web	This is an animal, that eats other living things.
producer	You get this when you draw lots of food chains together.
consumer	The arrows in a food chain show this.
energy flow	This is a plant, that catches light energy from the Sun.

2 Look at the food web above. Copy and complete these food chains.

cereal plants → _____ → humans

_____ → cows → _____

water plants → _____ → humans

3 a Write down three parts of a plant where food is stored.

b Write down three reasons why plants store food.

c Name a carnivore.

d Name a herbivore.

For your notes:

- Plants can store food in their roots, stems, fruit and seeds.

- Plants store food to help them survive in the winter, and to help their seeds grow.

- Humans are in many food chains, and these join up to make a food web.

33

Learn about:
● How plants grow best
● Nutrients and fertiliser

D2 Make them grow

Clever greenhouses

When you buy someone flowers, they have probably been grown in a greenhouse like the one below. It's specially designed to provide perfect conditions for plants to photosynthesise and grow.

To grow properly, plants need the right amount of:

● light
● warmth
● carbon dioxide.
● water
● nutrients from the soil

a For what process do the plants use carbon dioxide, light and water?

Automatic shades control the amount of light.

An automatic window and an automatic heater control the temperature.

Carbon dioxide is added to the air in the greenhouse for plants to use for photosynthesis.

A computer measures the water in the soil and switches on water sprinklers when it gets too dry.

Fertiliser is added to the water to give extra nutrients for growth.

Greenhouses are designed to let you produce more and better crops over a longer season.

When things go wrong

Some people don't like greenhouses. They think they are expensive, and that vegetables from them have no flavour. Sometimes the greenhouse equipment can go wrong. Look at these pictures showing what happens to the plants when it does.

b What happens to a plant that lacks:
(i) carbon dioxide?
(ii) water?

c Write a list of advantages of using a greenhouse to grow crops.

d Write a list of disadvantages of using a greenhouse to grow crops.

The shades stayed across the window all day for a month, making it very dark in the greenhouse.

The carbon dioxide ran out and no one noticed.

Someone unplugged the computer that controls the water. The plants were without water for two weeks.

What's in fertiliser?

Some plants need more nutrients than others. Some soils have very few nutrients. Farmers often add fertiliser to the soil to give extra nutrients to plants. Look at these fertiliser labels.

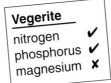

Vegerite
nitrogen	✔
phosphorus	✔
magnesium	✗

Vegemeet
nitrogen	✔
phosphorus	✔
magnesium	✗

Vegetreet
nitrogen	✔
phosphorus	✗
magnesium	✔

e **Make a list of nutrients that fertiliser can supply.**

If plants don't get enough of particular nutrients they become unhealthy. We say they are deficient. The pictures below show what happens.

Nutrient	nitrogen	phosphorus	magnesium
Why plants need it	Helps to make protein, which is important for growth.	Helps to make roots.	Helps to make chlorophyll.
What happens if plants are deficient	The plant grows slowly and has small pale leaves.	The roots and stem are short, and the leaves look purple.	The plant looks yellow or brown and cannot photosynthesise well.

f **What happens if a plant does not get enough nitrogen?**

g **What happens if a plant does not get enough magnesium?**

Fertilisers help plants grow larger, so farmers can make more money when they harvest and sell their crop. Using fertiliser can be expensive though.

- An alternative to fertiliser is manure. Manure contains many of the same nutrients as fertiliser.

- Apart from buying petrol for the tractor, and paying someone to drive it, manure is free because it comes from farm animals.

Questions

1 Match each word below with the reason why it is important to a plant. Write out each word with its correct reason.

Words	Reasons
fertiliser	helps a plant to grow
nitrogen	needed for photosynthesis
light	provides a plant with extra nutrients
carbon dioxide	needed for photosynthesis

2 What happens to a plant that does not get enough:

   a light?   **b** phosphorus?

3 Write a newspaper advertisement for the *Farming Times* for a fertiliser that contains nitrogen, phosphorus and magnesium. Include information describing why plants need these nutrients.

For your notes:

- To grow well, plants need the right amount of light, water and carbon dioxide for photosynthesis.

- There are advantages and disadvantages to growing plants in greenhouses.

- Plants need nutrients to stay healthy and grow. **Fertilisers** provide plants with extra nutrients.

D3 Competing plants

What do farmers think of weeds?

Weeds are plants that grow where you don't want them to grow. They need the same resources as my crop plants, so they **compete** with them. If they were animals, they'd fight for the resources. But weeds compete with my crops in far more sneaky ways …

Weeds grow tall to catch the light before it reaches the plants below.

They also grow longer roots to take in water and nutrients from the soil before the other plants can get them.

ⓐ What are weeds?

ⓑ How does being tall help weeds compete for light?

ⓒ How does having long and widely spread roots help weeds compete for water and nutrients?

Getting rid of weeds

Andrew used to work in the city, but moved to the countryside to become a farmer. He did not know anything about weeds and did not do anything to get rid of them. Look at the bar charts. Andrew's crop yields were lower than those of his neighbours, so they gave him some advice.

Maria: *It's much easier and cheaper to use **weedkiller**. If Andrew pulls up the weeds by hand, he'd need about 20 people working for him.*

John: *He should pull up all the weeds by hand.*

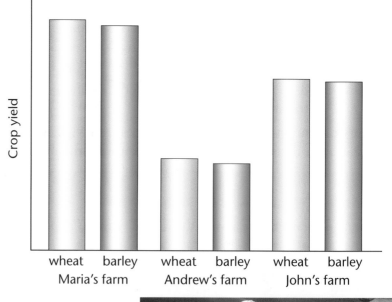

Crop yield

| wheat | barley | wheat | barley | wheat | barley |
| Maria's farm | | Andrew's farm | | John's farm | |

ⓓ Why do farmers want to get rid of weeds?

ⓔ Why do most farmers use weedkiller, rather than pulling up the weeds by hand?

Most weedkillers are **selective**, which means they only affect the plant you want to kill. You can spray the weedkiller all over a field of crops, and it will only kill the weeds.

What about the environment

Farmers kill weeds to get a good crop. But killing weeds can have unwanted effects on food webs. Look at the diagram on the right. It shows a food web in a sugar beet field. Fat hen is a weed that often grows in sugar beet fields. Skylarks, partridges and pheasants eat fat hen seeds.

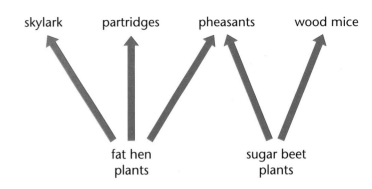

skylark   partridges   pheasants   wood mice

fat hen plants   sugar beet plants

f What would happen to the fat hen plant if weedkiller was sprayed on this field?

g What would happen to the numbers of skylarks and partridges?

h If the pheasants could not get food from fat hen plants, what would they eat for food?

Some people feel very strongly about protecting the environment. They won't eat any food that has been grown using artificial chemicals. They think that artificial fertilisers and weedkillers are unhealthy, and that **organic** food is better for you.

Organic food is grown using only natural products. Organic farmers don't use artificial weedkillers or fertilisers. Instead they employ more farm workers, so their crops cost more in the shops.

Questions

1 Copy and join up these half-sentences using the words below.

because   **otherwise**   **compete**   **in**

Weedkiller is good …	… for light and resources.
Weedkillers are selective, …	… it gets rid of weeds.
Weedkiller gets rid of plants that …	… they would kill the crop as well.
Weedkiller can affect food webs …	… an unexpected way.

2 Organic farmers don't use artificial weedkillers. What are:

  a the good things

  b the bad things about using weedkillers?

3 Explain how weedkillers can affect other organisms in a food web.

For your notes:

- **Weeds** are plants that **compete** with other plants for light, water and nutrients.

- Farmers kill weeds using **weedkiller**.

- **Organic** farmers don't use artificial chemicals.

- Removing one weed species from a food web can affect other members of the food web.

Learn about:
● How pests affect plant growth
● How poisons build up in food chains

D4 What a pest!

Who's a pest?

Field mice feed on farmers' crops. They compete with humans directly for food. Look at the food web below. Field mice compete with humans for wheat and barley.

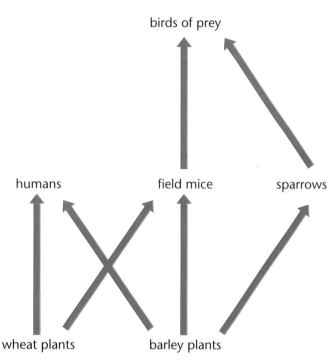

Any organisms such as field mice, greenfly or slugs that feed on farmers' crops are called **pests**. They tend to invade a field in huge numbers because there is a good supply of food there for them.

a Which two animals in the food web are pests?

These animals are all pests.

Getting rid of pests

John puts out traps to kill field mice, because they eat his crops. Because most pests come in big numbers, it's easier to use chemicals to kill them. These chemicals are called **pesticides**.

Many pests are insects, which can be killed by **insecticides**. A selective insecticide kills a particular type of insect. **Non-selective** insecticides kill any insect, whether they're a pest or not.

I have to kill pests. If I didn't, they would eat lots of my crop and I'd lose lots of money and go out of business.

b What is the difference between a pesticide and an insecticide?

What about the rest of the food chain?

Insecticides kill insects which are food for birds like bluetits and sparrows. These pyramids of numbers show the numbers of organisms before and after killing the insects. Even though bluetits are not pests, the insecticide could make them die from starvation.

c What would be the effect on the insects if the farmer put up nesting boxes to encourage more bluetits to the farm?

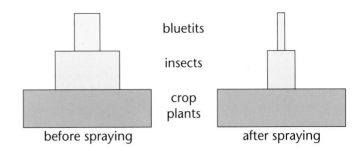

before spraying   after spraying

bluetits

insects

crop plants

1

2

3

4

Insecticides in the food chain

Greenfly feed on rose bushes. Look at what happens when you spray a rose bush with an insecticide to kill the greenfly.

1 Most of the greenfly die. But some absorb only a little insecticide, and survive.

2 Some insecticides do not break down, but are stored in the greenflies' bodies.

3 Bluetits eat greenfly. They may eat a lot of greenfly, getting a tiny dose of insecticide from each one.

4 Sparrowhawks eat bluetits. When a sparrowhawk eats lots of bluetits, it gets thousands of tiny doses of insecticide. This poisons the sparrowhawk.

Sparrowhawks are at the top end of the food chain. There are fewer bluetits than greenfly, and even fewer sparrowhawks than bluetits. The insecticide from thousands of greenfly ends up in one sparrowhawk. The build-up of insecticide poisons and kills the sparrowhawks.

d Which organisms in this food chain would have the highest levels of insecticide?

rose bush → insects → birds → cats

Questions

1 Look at this food chain:

barley → sawflies → pheasants → humans

a One of the animals in the food chain is a pest. Which one is it?

b A farmer sprayed the barley with insecticide to kill the sawflies. Why did the number of pheasants go down as well?

c When sawflies eat barley, they get a tiny dose of insecticide. Why does each human eventually get a much bigger dose?

2 What is the difference between a selective insecticide and a non-selective insecticide?

For your notes:

- **Pests** are animals such as insects that eat farmers' crops.

- Killing pests may have unexpected and unwanted effects in other parts of the food web.

- Poisons can build up along food chains and kill organisms at the top end of the food chain.

D5 How many?

Counting wild animals

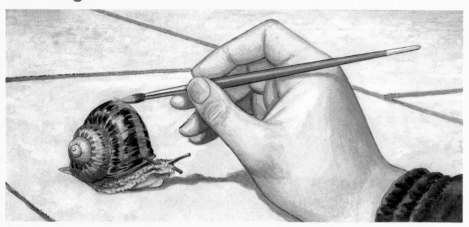

Some scientists were doing research in a tropical rainforest. They wanted to know how many snails were living on an island in the middle of a lake in the forest. They sampled the snails. The flow chart on the right shows how they did this. From their samples, they **estimated** the number of snails on the island (the population).

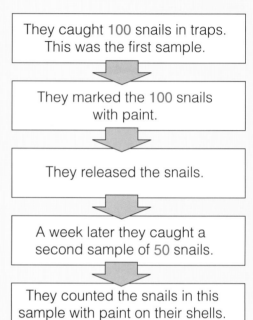

They caught 100 snails in traps. This was the first sample.

They marked the 100 snails with paint.

They released the snails.

A week later they caught a second sample of 50 snails.

They counted the snails in this sample with paint on their shells. There were 10.

● snails painted = 100

● painted snails caught again = 10

● 'painted snails caught again' : 'total snails painted' = 10 : 100 = 1 : 10

● The ratio 1 : 10 means there are always 10 snails out there for every 1 snail caught.

● So when they caught 50 snails, they multiplied by 10 and estimated there were 50 × 10 = 500 snails on the island. The population of snails was 500.

You can write these bullet points down in shorthand like this:

10 : 100 = 1:10
= 50 : population

So how do you know what to write instead of population? Well, the first ratio says there are always 10 snails in the forest for every one snail caught. When they caught 50 snails in the second sample, they estimated that there were 50 × 10 = 500 snails in the rainforest. The population of snails was 500.

a How many snails were marked with paint?

b How many of these snails were caught again (recaptured)?

c What was the ratio of 'painted snails recaptured' : 'total snails painted'?

d What was the size of the second sample of snails?

e How many snails were on the island?

Studying pollution

Another group of scientists noticed that an oil company had built an oil-drilling platform right next to the lake where the snails lived. They knew that oil platforms sometimes release polluted water, and they wanted to check whether the water was harming the fish in the lake. To find out, they studied the fish in this lake and in another lake, which did not have an oil-drilling platform.

The scientists sampled the fish at each site. The flow chart on the right shows what they did. They repeated this every two years for ten years. They used different-shaped notches each time.

f **Copy this table and work out the populations for 1988, 1990, 1992, 1994 and 1996 for both sites.**

Code: fish marked with notches = 500
number of notched fish caught again
sample size
population (what you need to work out)

```
They caught 500 fish.
        ↓
They cut a notch in a fin on
each fish.
        ↓
They released the fish.
        ↓
One month later they caught
a second sample of 100 fish.
        ↓
They counted the number
of fish with notches.
        ↓
They used ratios to estimate
the population of fish.
```

Site	1988	1990	1992	1994	1996
1 oil-drilling platform	5 5:500 = 1:100 = 100:? ? = ...	23 23:500 = 1:21.7 = 100:? ? = ...	36 36:500 = 1:13.9 = 100:? ? = ...	48 48:500 = 1:10.4 = 100:? ? = ...	50 50:500 = 1:10 = 100:? ? = ...
2 no oil-drilling platform	5 5:500 = 1:100 = 100:? ? = ...	5 5:500 = 1:100 = 100:? ? = ...	5 5:500 = 1:100 = 100:? ? = ...	5 5:500 = 1:100 = 100:? ? = ...	5 5:500 = 1:100 = 100:? ? = ...

g **Make a bar chart for each site. Set out the bar chart as shown on the right.**

h **Look at the two bar charts. Did the oil-drilling platform affect the population of fish?**

Questions

Think about the scientists' pollution research.

1 Why did the scientists study one site without an oil-drilling platform?

2 Suggest two things other than pollution that could change the population of fish.

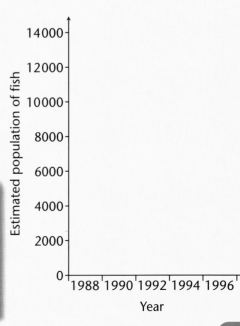

41

What is a metal?

Particles 1

Are they useful?

Metals are very important in our lives. As you can see from this photo, lots of things around us are made of metals.

Did you know?

Stone Age people found pieces of gold in rivers.

Properties

Carly works as a courier for a mail order company. Her motorcycle is mainly made of metals. How a metal is used depends on how it behaves. We call this the metal's 'properties'. Look at the useful properties of the metals used in Carly's motorcycle.

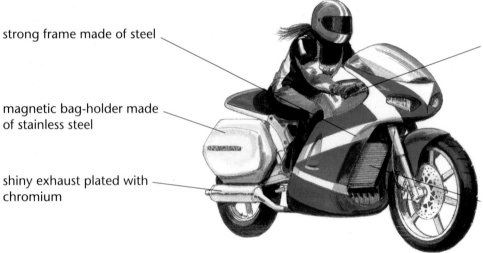

strong frame made of steel

magnetic bag-holder made of stainless steel

shiny exhaust plated with chromium

electrical circuits with copper wiring

radiator made of steel to conduct heat energy from the bike to the air

ⓐ **Look at this picture above. Which properties of metals do you think have been used in Carly's motorcycle?**

Gold and silver are used for jewellery because they are shiny. Steel is used to make bridges and large buildings because it is strong. Iron is used for magnets because it is magnetic. We discover the properties of a material by asking questions such as, 'Does electricity pass through it?' or 'What temperature does it melt at?'

Do metals conduct electricity?

You can use metals to complete a circuit because they let electricity pass through them: they **conduct** electricity. Most wires are made of copper. The cables between electricity pylons are made of aluminium. Non-metals are poor conductors of electricity.

ⓑ **Why is plastic used to cover electric wires?**

Do metals conduct thermal energy?

We make saucepans of copper, cast iron, stainless steel and aluminium. Metals let heat pass through them easily. They conduct thermal (heat) energy. Non-metals are poor conductors of thermal (heat) energy.

c Why are many saucepan handles made of plastic?

What are metals made of?

Metal things are either made of one metallic element or are mixtures of metals and other elements. For example, iron is an element; steel is a mixture of iron and some carbon.

Solid, liquid or gas?

Most metals are solids at room temperature (25 °C) – the temperature we are comfortable living at. Mercury is the only metal which isn't a solid at room temperature. Non-metals can be solids, liquids or gases.

d Which other metal is a liquid at 100 °C?

e Which metal is a solid even in the hottest part of a Bunsen burner flame (1500 °C)?

Physical and chemical properties

The properties of metals described on these pages are physical properties. In the rest of this unit, you will look at the chemical properties of metals and metal compounds. You will find out how they react, following some patterns. One example you have already met is that elements react with oxygen to make oxides.

Do you remember?

Elements contain only one sort of atom. In the periodic table, the elements that have similar properties are grouped together.

Metal	Melting point in °C
sodium	98
magnesium	650
mercury	−39
calcium	850
iron	1535
copper	1080
aluminium	660
tin	232
lead	327
zinc	419
silver	961

Questions

1 **a** Name a metal used in electrical wires.

  b Name a metal used to make saucepans.

  c Name a metal that is magnetic.

2 Choose one of the metals mentioned on this spread and prepare a fact file on it. Include its properties and main uses. Use poems or cartoons.

3 **a** Give an example of a material that does not conduct electricity or thermal energy.

  b How might this non-conductor be used in a kitchen?

4 Write a poem about metals. Include as many properties as you can.

For your notes:

● Metals are shiny and strong. A few metals, including iron, are magnetic.

● Metals are good conductors of electricity and thermal (heat) energy.

● Most metals are solids at room temperature.

E2 Salt on the roads

What is salt?

Every time icy roads are treated with salt, crystals of sodium chloride are sprinkled over them. In science, there are lots of different **salts** – sodium chloride is just one of them! Some salts are made by neutralising an acid with an alkali. Some metals form metal hydroxides. Some metal hydroxides are soluble in water and are called alkalis.

Neutralising an acid with an alkali.

The reaction

When an acid is neutralised by an alkali, a salt and water are made. Neutralisation is a chemical reaction. The reaction between sodium hydroxide and hydrochloric acid makes sodium chloride (common salt) and water. The word equation for this reaction is:

> sodium hydroxide + hydrochloric acid → sodium chloride + water

The substances that react are called the reactants. The substances that are made in a chemical reaction are called the products. The reactants are on the left of the word equation; the products are on the right.

ⓐ **Explain the meaning of the word neutralisation.**

Making salts

If you take solutions of sodium hydroxide and hydrochloric acid that have the same concentration, and mix equal volumes of them, the sodium hydroxide neutralises the acid.

It is important to use the correct amounts of acid and alkali in a neutralisation reaction. You can use an indicator or a pH meter to test for neutralisation. If you test the solution for pH at the exact point of neutralisation, the solution will be pH 7, which is neutral. (In fact, this is very difficult to do in practice.)

If you leave the neutral solution to evaporate, you will see crystals of salts. Using sodium hydroxide and hydrochloric acid, you get the salt they put on the roads!

Making other salts

There are lots of different types of salts. If you use other acids and alkalis, you get different salts. You can write a general word equation for the neutralisation reaction:

> acid + alkali → salt + water
> reactants   products

Naming the products

A chemical reaction rearranges some of the atoms in the reactants to make the products. You can work out the name of the products by some rearranging too.

To name a salt, start by taking the name of the metal from the alkali. For sodium hydroxide, take the name of the metal – sodium. The second part comes from the acid – hydrochloric acid makes chloride salts. So the salt is sodium chloride.

b What pH would you expect if hydrochloric acid had been neutralised by sodium hydroxide solution?

c What do you think would happen if you mix different volumes of sodium hydroxide and hydrochloric acid which have the same concentrations?

d If you neutralise hydrochloric acid with potassium hydroxide, what salt will be made?

e Name the salt you would get if you reacted magnesium hydroxide with hydrochloric acid.

Questions

1 Copy and complete these word equations.

> sodium hydroxide + hydrochloric acid → _____ + water

> potassium hydroxide + hydrochloric acid → _____ + _____

2 **a** Draw a flow chart explaining how to make sodium chloride from sodium hydroxide and hydrochloric acid.

b Draw a diagram to show one way of removing the water from a salt after a neutralisation reaction.

3 Adam claimed that there was only one salt. Write an argument to convince him that he is wrong.

4 Name the salt you would get by neutralising hydrochloric acid with copper hydroxide.

For your notes:

- Alkalis neutralise acids to make a **salt** and water.

- The name of the salt comes from the names of the acid and the metal in the alkali used to make it. Hydrochloric acid makes chloride salts.

E3 Acids attack metals

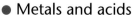
Disappearing metals?

The photo on the right shows part of an old car exhaust pipe. It has been corroded by the acidic gases from the exhaust.

Zinc and acids

If you add a few granules of zinc to some hydrochloric acid or sulphuric acid, it fizzes. The zinc is corroded and bubbles of hydrogen form. When all of the zinc has been used up, the bubbles stop.

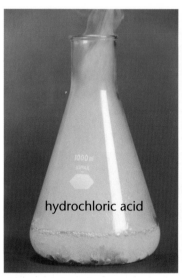

hydrochloric acid

sulphuric acid

a How do you know that a chemical reaction has taken place?

As well as hydrogen, the other products of the reactions are salts called zinc sulphate and zinc chloride.

The word equation for the reaction between zinc and sulphuric acid is:

> zinc + sulphuric acid → zinc sulphate + hydrogen

The word equation for the reaction between zinc and hydrochloric acid is:

> zinc + hydrochloric acid → zinc chloride + hydrogen

b Which salt is made when calcium reacts with sulphuric acid?

As with bases neutralising acids, at the end of a 'metal + acid' reaction you may be left with a salt solution. Some salts dissolve in the water from the acid. You can evaporate the water to get solid salt crystals. If the salt does not dissolve in water, you can separate it by filtering.

You can write a general word equation for the reaction between metals and acids:

> metal + acid → salt + hydrogen
> reactants   products

Do you remember?

Metals are often corroded away by acids. They react to produce new substances.

Do you remember?

Some metals react with acids to make hydrogen gas. We can collect a test tube full of the gas and test it by putting a lighted splint near the top. Hydrogen is explosive, so you will hear a 'pop'!

Did you know?

When sulphuric acid reacts with metals it makes sulphates.

Acids contain hydrogen

All acids contain hydrogen. This is where the hydrogen gas comes from when acids react with metals. The name of one acid gives us a clue about this.

c Which acid has part of the word 'hydrogen' in its name?

Hydrochloric acid contains hydrogen and chlorine and gets its name from both of these.

Different metals

Jade did an experiment to investigate what happens when iron and tin are added to dilute sulphuric acid.

d Which metal did not react with sulphuric acid?

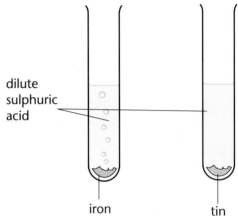

dilute sulphuric acid

iron   tin

Tin cans?

Lots of food and drinks contain acids. Some cans for food and drinks are made from steel with a coating of tin on the inside. Steel is made from iron and might react with the acids in food. Tin reacts very slowly with dilute acids.

Other cans are made of aluminium, which reacts with oxygen in the air, forming a layer of aluminium oxide. This protective layer means that aluminium cans can be used for storing acidic food. They are also safe for use with other food or drink.

Questions

1 Copy and complete the word equations.

   a iron + sulphuric acid → _____ _____ + hydrogen

   b magnesium + sulphuric acid → magnesium _____ + _____

2 What do you think would happen if you put an iron nail into a beaker of hydrochloric acid?

3 Describe the test for hydrogen.

For your notes:

- Many metals react with acids and are corroded away.

- When an acid reacts with a metal, a salt and hydrogen gas are produced.

- The test for hydrogen is to put a lighted splint near the top of a test tube full of the gas. You will hear a 'pop'.

Acids attack carbonates

Limestone rocks

York Minster is built from limestone – mainly calcium carbonate. Over the years this has reacted with naturally acidic rain water, causing some of the surface of the building to be chemically weathered.

> ### Do you remember?
> Metals form compounds called carbonates. Acids react with metal carbonates. These are neutralisation reactions.

Indigestion

Some indigestion tablets contain calcium carbonate. They fizz when you add them to acid. Calcium carbonate reacts with stomach acid to neutralise it. A salt and water are made, just as when any other base neutralises an acid. But there is also a third product – a gas.

ⓐ **Which gas is produced when calcium carbonate reacts with acid?**
(*Hint*: look at the name 'carbonate'.)

Your stomach makes hydrochloric acid, which helps to digest your food. Sometimes the stomach produces too much acid, so you get indigestion.

Carbonates and acids

The word 'carbonate' tells us that this part of the compound has carbon and oxygen atoms in it. They stay together until the neutralisation reaction splits them up. They come together again to make carbon dioxide gas. The carbon and the oxygen atoms come from the carbonate.

> ### Do you remember?
> The test for carbon dioxide is to bubble the gas through limewater. The limewater turns milky.

Naming the products

You can work out the name of the salt as you did before (see page 45). Take the name of the metal from the carbonate. For example, take calcium from calcium carbonate. The type of salt depends on the acid used. Hydrochloric acid makes chloride salts. So the salt is calcium chloride.

The word equation for the reaction is:

calcium carbonate	+	hydrochloric acid	→	calcium chloride	+	water	+	carbon dioxide

You can write a general word equation for the reaction of metal carbonates with acids:

metal carbonate + acid → salt + water + carbon dioxide
reactants   products

b What are the three products made when a carbonate neutralises an acid?

Testing carbonates

This pupil set up an experiment to find out if other metal carbonates reacted with acids. He added some green copper carbonate to sulphuric acid and bubbled the gas through limewater.

He noticed:

- the reactants fizzed
- the colour changed to blue
- the limewater turned milky
- the boiling tube felt hotter.

His first three observations showed that new materials were produced. The boiling tube getting hotter showed that energy was released. All these observations are evidence of a chemical reaction taking place.

c Which salt did he make?

d Write a word equation for the reaction.

Did you know?

The white substance that you get in kettles and toilets in some parts of the country is called limescale. It is calcium carbonate. Some toilet cleaners have acid in them to neutralise and get rid of the limescale.

Questions

1 These are the names of substances in a reaction between an acid and a metal carbonate.

   **sodium carbonate   sodium chloride   hydrochloric acid
   carbon dioxide   water**

   a Put the names in order and write a word equation for the reaction.

   b Label the reactants and the products.

   c Name the salt that is produced.

2 **a** You want to find out whether copper carbonate reacts with hydrochloric acid in the same way as it does with sulphuric acid. What apparatus would you use? Draw a labelled diagram.

   b What would you look for as evidence of a chemical reaction taking place?

3 Write a word equation for the reaction between copper carbonate and hydrochloric acid.

For your notes:

- Metal carbonates neutralise acids, making a salt, water and carbon dioxide gas.

- The test for carbon dioxide is to bubble it through limewater. The limewater turns milky.

- New materials and energy changes are evidence of chemical reactions.

E5 Acids and metal oxides

Learn about:
- Metal oxides and acids

Particles 2

Stopping rust

Rust can be a problem on bikes and cars. The chemical name for rust is iron oxide. You can buy rust removers that contain acid. The acid reacts with iron oxide on the surface of iron or steel objects. This leaves a clean surface that you can paint. But it means you have lost a little of the iron at the surface.

ⓐ How do rust removers work?

Rust remover contains acid.

Oxides reacting

Metal oxides are bases. They neutralise acids. Black copper oxide reacts with dilute sulphuric acid if you heat it. A blue solution of copper sulphate is formed. If you leave the solution so the water evaporates, you will see blue crystals of copper sulphate. The crystals are a different colour to those you started with. This is evidence that a new substance is produced.

Do you remember?

You can separate a mixture of insoluble and soluble solids by dissolving it in water and then filtering out the insoluble solid. You can separate a solute from a solution by evaporating the solvent (water).

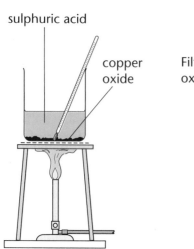

sulphuric acid

copper oxide

Filter out any oxide that is left.

Leave the solution to evaporate.

ⓑ Look at this diagram. What process is used to:
   (i) separate any copper oxide that is left after the reaction?
   (ii) get copper sulphate crystals from copper sulphate solution?

The word equation for the reaction is:

> copper oxide + sulphuric acid → copper sulphate + water

You can write a general word equation for the reaction of oxides with acids:

> metal oxide + acid → salt + water

ⓒ Why do you think this reaction did not produce bubbles?

Did you know?

Old copper coins look black because they are covered with black copper oxide. If you put them in vinegar (an acid), the copper oxide reacts with the acid to give you shiny coins in mint condition!

50

Copper sulphate is a useful salt. It is used to spray grapevines to prevent disease.

Copper sulphate crystals.

Time to investigate

Laxatives are medicines that relieve constipation. Some laxative medicines are made from magnesium sulphate.

Lianne and Adam worked out that you could make magnesium sulphate by reacting magnesium oxide with sulphuric acid instead of copper oxide. They added some magnesium oxide to sulphuric acid. This time there was no colour change. They filtered the solution and evaporated it. White crystals of magnesium sulphate were left.

d **Write a word equation for this reaction.**

A magnesium sulphate crystal.

Questions

1 These are the names of substances in a reaction between an acid and a metal oxide.

water **sulphuric acid** **magnesium sulphate** **magnesium oxide**

  a Put the names in order to write a word equation.

  b Label the reactants and the products.

  c Name the salt that is produced.

2 What evidence is there that a chemical reaction takes place when you add copper oxide to sulphuric acid?

3 Calcium sulphate is used to make Plaster of Paris – the plaster you have if you break a bone.

  a Name the metal oxide and the acid you would need to make calcium sulphate.

  b Write a word equation for the reaction.

For your notes:

- Many metal oxides are bases. They react with acids, making a salt and water.

Particles 2

F1 Losing that shine

All that glitters ...

Gold is a beautiful shiny metal. It is perfect for jewellery but is very expensive. You can buy cheaper jewellery made from other metals. These look fine at first but soon lose their shine. Most metals lose their shine when they react with oxygen.

a Where does the oxygen come from?

When substances react with oxygen they form compounds called **oxides**.

Reactivity

Gold is a very **unreactive** metal. Gold jewellery can last thousands of years without changing, because it does not react with oxygen. Most other metals do react with oxygen, but some react faster than others. Iron reacts slowly with oxygen to make rust.

b What other substance is needed to make iron rust? (*Hint*: iron does not rust in the desert.)

c We paint iron to stop it rusting. How does that work?

Some metals react quickly with the oxygen in air. Potassium reacts with oxygen as soon as a newly cut surface is exposed to oxygen. So much heat energy is given out in this reaction that a lump of potassium will burst into flames if left in air. We say that potassium is a very **reactive** metal.

d Why do you think we store potassium covered in oil?

I thought that ring was made from real gold!

This potassium will lose its shine in seconds.

What is happening?

Potassium reacts with oxygen in the air to form potassium oxide, giving out lots of energy. The word equation for this reaction is:

potassium + oxygen → potassium oxide

e This is a chemical reaction. How can you tell?

How other metals react with oxygen

Zinc also reacts with the oxygen in air and will lose its shine after a while. But zinc does not give out as much energy as potassium when it reacts with oxygen. It can safely be left in the air without bursting into flames. Zinc is less reactive than potassium, but it will still burn if it is heated.

zinc + oxygen → zinc oxide

Zinc burns with a bright blue-white flame.

f **What do you think the white 'smoke' in the photo above is called? (*Hint*: it is a new chemical formed in the reaction.)**

Copper is not very reactive. It reacts much more slowly than zinc or iron. Even when it is heated, copper just forms a layer of black copper oxide that dulls the surface. But this is still more reactive than gold!

copper + oxygen → copper oxide

Copper does not burn, but it does react to form an oxide layer.

Questions

1 Copy and complete these sentences by choosing from the words in bold.

Gold stays shiny because it is a very **reactive/unreactive** metal.

Potassium has to be stored away from air because it is a very **reactive/unreactive** metal.

2 Use the information on this spread to help you list the metals copper, gold, zinc and potassium in order of reactivity. Start with the most reactive at the top.

3 Malcolm is investigating the reactivity of three metals: potassium, tin and copper. Malcolm's first idea is to heat a small piece of each material in a Bunsen burner flame.

   a Tin reacts when heated with oxygen to form a white powder. What do you think this new compound is called?

   b Write a word equation for this reaction.

   c Why is Malcolm's plan not safe? (Which part would be very dangerous?)

For your notes:

● Metals react with oxygen to make metal **oxides**.

● The more **reactive** the metal, the faster it reacts.

● The more reactive the metal, the more energy is released when it reacts.

Particles 2

F2 Corrosive liquids

Dangerous acids

Acids such as the dilute sulphuric acid used in car batteries are very strong and corrosive. They will dissolve many metals, producing explosive hydrogen gas and a salt. This careless mechanic could be making iron sulphate from his spanner!

How different metals react with acid

Hydrochloric acid reacts with metals to form chloride salts. Zinc fizzes steadily in hydrochloric acid as zinc chloride and hydrogen gas are made. The test tube warms up as heat energy is released in the reaction.

zinc + hydrochloric acid → zinc chloride + hydrogen

When magnesium reacts with hydrochloric acid, the bubbles of hydrogen are produced more quickly. This shows that magnesium is more reactive than zinc.

a **Write a word equation for magnesium reacting with hydrochloric acid.**

Copper is less reactive than zinc. In fact, it is so unreactive that it never reacts with an acid in this way.

b **Sue puts magnesium, copper and zinc into hydrochloric acid in separate test tubes. She measures the temperature rise in each. Which metal will give:**
(i) the greatest temperature rise?
(ii) the least temperature rise?

Do you remember?

In Unit E Reactions of metals and metal compounds you learnt how metals react with acids.

metal + acid → salt + hydrogen

Faster, not more!

John and Sue are reacting some metals with acid.

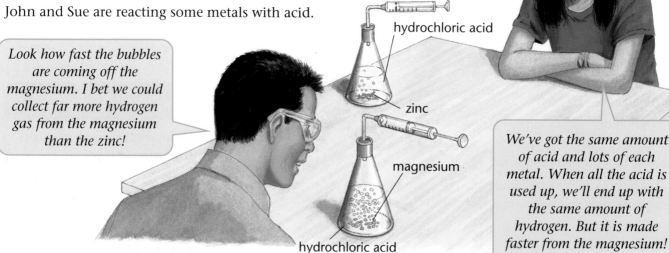

Look how fast the bubbles are coming off the magnesium. I bet we could collect far more hydrogen gas from the magnesium than the zinc!

hydrochloric acid

zinc

magnesium

hydrochloric acid

We've got the same amount of acid and lots of each metal. When all the acid is used up, we'll end up with the same amount of hydrogen. But it is made faster from the magnesium!

c **Sue is right, but how would you know when to compare the volumes?**

Some metals react with water

A small piece of potassium dropped into water reacts in a most spectacular way. The potassium and water react to form potassium hydroxide and hydrogen gas. Look at the photo on the left. So much energy is given out that the gas catches fire!

> potassium + water → potassium hydroxide + hydrogen

Sodium reacts in a similar way, but not quite as violently as potassium. Even so, the sodium gets so hot it melts and whizzes across the surface. Sodium hydroxide is made.

Sodium in water also produces a flame if it is trapped on filter paper.

(d) **Write a word equation for the reaction of sodium with water.**

Calcium also reacts with water. Look at the photo below on the right. Less energy is produced than when sodium reacts, so it is safe to do the reaction in a test tube rather than an open container.

> calcium + water → calcium hydroxide + hydrogen

Acids always give a much stronger reaction than water with a metal. Most other metals either react very slowly with water or are not affected at all.

(e) **Write down the name of a metal that would not be affected by water at all.**

Calcium in water.

Questions

1 Copy and complete the word equations using these salts.

   calcium chloride   iron sulphate   magnesium sulphate

   iron + sulphuric acid → _____ + hydrogen

   magnesium + sulphuric acid → _____ + hydrogen

   calcium + hydrochloric acid → _____ + hydrogen

2 Sue is investigating the reactivity of metals by putting them in dilute sulphuric acid. She would like to include copper, magnesium and sodium in her investigation.

   a Suggest which metal is too dangerous for Sue to use. (She can replace it with zinc.)

   b Predict the outcome of Sue's experiment.

      (i) Which metals will react?

      (ii) Which will react most quickly?

3 John is doing a project on metals. He wrote that potassium is so reactive it has to be stored under water to stop it from reacting with the air. Explain why that would not be a good idea.

For your notes:

- Some metals react with acid to make hydrogen and a salt.

- Very reactive metals react with water to make hydrogen and a metal hydroxide.

Displacement reactions

Look at this photo. If you hang a copper wire in a colourless solution of silver nitrate, the solution gradually turns blue. Beautiful crystals of silver metal grow out from the wire.

The copper is more reactive than silver and pushes the silver from its compound. The copper particles take the place of the silver particles, moving them out of the way. This is called a **displacement reaction**.

copper +	silver nitrate	→	silver	+ copper nitrate
brown solid	colourless solution		silvery solid	blue solution

ⓐ The solution got warmer during this reaction. Why was that?

Who's the most attractive?

There is a simple model you can use to help you understand this type of reaction. Silver and nitrate make a happy couple – until copper comes along. Copper is more 'attractive' than silver, so nitrate pairs up with copper instead. The silver atoms go off on their own.

The more reactive a metal is, the more it 'attractive' it is, and so more likely to pair up with other particles and form a compound. Any metal can be pushed out of its compounds by a more reactive metal.

silver nitrate

copper

copper nitrate

silver

ⓑ An iron nail gets coated with copper if you dip it into copper sulphate.
(i) Explain why this happens.
(ii) Write a word equation for the reaction.

Who gets the oxygen?

If you gently heat a mixture of zinc and copper oxide they react together, giving out a lot of thermal (heat) energy. Zinc is more reactive than copper and so is able to displace it from the compound. In this reaction, the oxide finds zinc more attractive and copper goes off on its own!

zinc + copper oxide → zinc oxide + copper

c If you heat the zinc oxide and the copper, will you get the zinc back? (If not, why not?)

Do you remember?

Iron rusts when it reacts with air and water.

Using displacement to stop rusting

When iron rusts it reacts with oxygen to make iron oxide. Putting a more reactive metal such as zinc against the iron can stop rusting. The zinc then reacts with the oxygen instead of the iron.

d Which is more likely to form a metal oxide, zinc or iron? Give a reason for your answer.

This method of preventing iron rusting is used for ships, submarines and oil rigs. Huge lumps of reactive metal are fixed onto the sides. Oxygen then reacts with this metal instead of the iron.

Questions

1 Copy and complete this sentence by choosing from the words in bold.

A **more/less** reactive metal can displace a **more/less** reactive metal from its compound.

2 Magnesium is more reactive than nickel. Nickel chloride makes a green solution. Magnesium chloride makes a colourless solution.

  a Write a word equation for the reaction that occurs when a strip of magnesium is placed in nickel chloride solution.

  b What would you observe during this reaction?

3 Powdered aluminium will react with iron oxide. This is like the reaction between zinc and copper oxide. Melted iron and aluminium oxide are made in the reaction.

  a Which is the more reactive metal, aluminium or iron? Give reasons for your answer.

  b Write a word equation for the reaction

  c Why is the iron melted, rather than solid?

For your notes:

- More reactive metals push less reactive metals out of their compounds. These reactions are called **displacement reactions**.

- In a displacement reaction, the more reactive metal ends up in the compound.

- Displacement reactions can be useful.

- Displacement reactions often release a lot of energy.

F4 Who's top of the league?

Particles 2

The reactivity series

The **reactivity series** is a list of metals. The most reactive is at the top and the least reactive is at the bottom. Joel is putting 10 metals into a reactivity series. The 10 metals are calcium (Ca), copper (Cu), gold (Au), iron (Fe), lithium (Li), magnesium (Mg), nickel (Ni), zinc (Zn), sodium (Na) and potassium (K).

a Joel looks at samples of the 10 metals. Sodium and potassium are stored under oil. Does that mean they are reactive or unreactive?

Reaction with water

Joel finds a video that shows sodium, lithium and potassium reacting with cold water. All three react, and all three reactions make hydrogen. Lithium reacts the slowest and potassium reacts the fastest, with sodium in-between. He writes them in order of reactivity.

potassium
sodium
lithium

Joel then decides to check the reactivity of all the metals with cold water. He cannot use potassium and sodium as they are too dangerous. His teacher agrees that lithium will be safe enough to test, as long as he uses a very small piece. He has to do the reaction in a beaker, not a test tube. Joel puts a bit of each metal into cold water in a small beaker. This table shows his results.

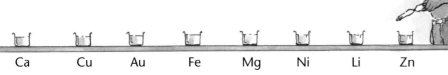

Ca   Cu   Au   Fe   Mg   Ni   Li   Zn

Metal	Observation
calcium	many bubbles, made quickly
copper	no reaction
gold	no reaction
iron	no reaction
lithium	most bubbles, made very quickly
magnesium	a few bubbles, made very slowly
nickel	no reaction
zinc	no reaction

b Which metals reacted with cold water in Joel's experiment?

c Put these metals in order of reactivity, with the most reactive at the top.

Reaction with dilute acid

Joel decides to react the metals with hydrochloric acid. Calcium and lithium are far too reactive to try, so Joel tests copper, gold, iron, magnesium, nickel and zinc with hydrochloric acid. Magnesium bubbled the most, followed by zinc, but Joel was surprised that the others did not seem to react at all.

Joel can now write a reactivity series for six of the metals like this.

potassium
sodium
lithium
calcium
magnesium
zinc

Displacement reactions

Joel is still not sure of the order of the last four metals: copper (Cu), gold (Au), iron (Fe) and nickel (Ni). He decides to use displacement reactions to sort them out.

For his experiment Joel uses copper sulphate, iron sulphate and nickel sulphate solutions. He records the experiment in this table.
He adds the three metals to the solutions. If there is a colour change, then a reaction happened. No colour change means no reaction. Joel ticks the combinations that had reacted.

Metal compound	Metal		
	nickel	copper	iron
nickel sulphate		before after	before after ✓
copper sulphate	before after ✓		before after ✓
iron sulphate	before after	before after	

d Which metal pushed nickel out of the nickel sulphate?

e Which metals pushed copper out of the copper sulphate?

f Out of copper, iron and nickel, which is:
   (i) the most reactive metal?
   (ii) the least reactive metal?

Joel tries putting some gold metal with each of the sulphate solutions. The gold does not push any of the other metals from their compounds. This shows that gold is the least reactive metal.

g Write a reactivity series for all 10 metals.

Questions

1 Joel reacted lithium with water in one of his experiments.

   a Why was Joel allowed to use only a very small piece of lithium?

   b Why was it safer to use a small beaker rather than a test tube when reacting lithium with water?

   c What other safety precautions would Joel have taken when doing the experiments?

2 Sam put some copper coins in silver nitrate solution. After some time, the coins went silvery, and the solution started to have a slight green-blue colour.

   a Is silver below or above copper in the reactivity series? Give reasons for your answer.

   b When ancient jewellery is dug up, silver items are badly corroded but gold ones look 'as new'. Is silver above or below gold in the reactivity series?

   c Would a gold coin become coated with silver when placed in silver nitrate solution? Give a reason for your answer.

For your notes:

● The **reactivity series** is a list of metals with the most reactive at the top and the least reactive at the bottom.

F5 Reactivity in action

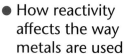
Learn about:
- How the reactivity series can be used
- How reactivity affects the way metals are used

Particles 2

Mending a broken rail

A rail has cracked on the express railway line in open country. Molten iron is needed to fill the gap, but the melting point of iron is very high – over 1500 °C. How can you make a small amount of molten iron so far away from an energy source?

Tricky ...

... a wood or charcoal fire will not get hot enough to melt iron.

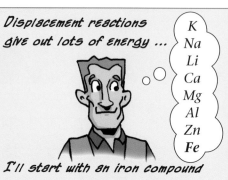

Displacement reactions give out lots of energy ...

K
Na
Li
Ca
Mg
Al
Zn
Fe

I'll start with an iron compound and find a much more reactive metal to push the iron out.

I've got it! Aluminium powder mixed with iron oxide should do the trick.

The aluminium will displace the iron and give out enough heat energy to melt it.

Spectacular displacement

If aluminium powder is mixed with iron oxide and given a kick-start of energy, a very spectacular displacement reaction occurs. The aluminium pushes the iron out of its compound and takes its place.

> aluminium + iron oxide → aluminium oxide + iron

So much energy is given out during this reaction that the iron melts. Look at this photo. If this mixture is reacted between the broken ends of a rail, molten iron fills the gap. When this sets, the rail is as good as new.

Do you remember?

Iron is a very useful metal but is high enough in the reactivity series to react with oxygen and water – it rusts! It has to be coated with paint to keep the oxygen and water out and stop it from rusting away.

a Magnesium is above aluminium in the reactivity series. Do you think it could be used instead of aluminium in this reaction? Explain your answer.

Bottom is best ...

Corrugated iron is cheap, strong and waterproof. It can be good for roofing, but over 20 or 30 years it just rusts away.

b Platinum is used for expensive jewellery. Do you think it is at the top or bottom of the reactivity series?

Copper is much less reactive than iron and does not react with acid. Copper is more expensive than iron, but copper roofs last much longer.

Copper's low position in the reactivity series also makes it useful for water pipes and tanks.

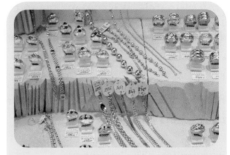

And don't forget that the metals at the bottom of the reactivity series, such as gold and silver, stay the shiniest!

Metals in rocks

The metal has to be extracted (got) from the ore using chemical reactions. The more reactive the metal, the more tightly it is joined in its compounds. It is more difficult to get the metal out of its ore. The less reactive the metal, the easier it is to get the metal out of its ore. Copper is not very reactive, and so the metal could have been made by accident in a fire, when copper ore reacted with carbon from wood. Aluminium ore does not react with carbon at all. It was discovered much later as it can only be made using electricity.

Did you know?

Metals are found in rocks. Gold is very rare but can be found as the shiny metal. Most other metals are found in compounds such as oxides. These are called the metal **ores**.

Questions

1 Copy and complete each sentence by choosing from the words below:

too reactive   not reactive enough

Magnesium is not used for roofing because it is _____.

Iron is not used for jewellery because it is _____.

2 Lead is a poisonous metal that is more reactive than copper. Suggest why it is no longer used to make water pipes.

3 Titanium is used to make replacement hip joints that have to survive for years inside the human body. Do you think titanium is reactive or unreactive?

For your notes:

- The reactivity series can be very useful for extracting metals from their compounds.
- The uses of metals depend on their reactivity.

F6 Variables together

Iron ...

Iron is the second most common metal in the Earth's crust. More iron is produced and used than all of the other metals put together. Iron is very strong. It is used to make cars, bridges, the skeletons of buildings, ships, nails and screws, steel cables, pans, radiators, bicycles and thousands of other items. There is more aluminium than iron in the Earth's crust. Unfortunately, it is expensive and difficult to remove from the Earth's crust.

a Why is iron used more than aluminium?

... rusts away!

But there's a problem. Iron rusts! Iron reacts with water and the oxygen in air, making flaky brown iron oxide. This breaks off, exposing fresh metal. So rusting can carry on until there is no metal left. Stopping rusting saves billions of pounds.

You need iron of course! And rust is a kind of iron oxide so you must need oxygen.

But iron only seem to rust if it gets wet, so water must be important …

Do you remember?

A variable is a thing that we change, or changes, in an investigation.

How can we stop iron rusting?

Before we can stop iron rusting, we have to understand the variables that affect the way iron rusts.

b What are the two variables that Terry and Tasha think might affect the way iron rusts?

Planning their experiment

Terry and Tasha decide to do an experiment to see which variable controls the way iron rusts. Terry wants to find out what effect oxygen has. To make it a fair test, he decides to keep water away from his iron nails. Tasha wants to find out what effect water has. To make it a fair test, she decides to keep oxygen away from her iron nails.

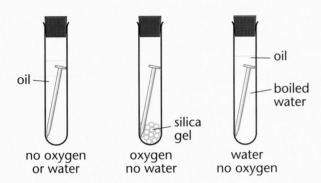

One week later they checked their nails. None of the nails had gone rusty!

c Why do you think the nails had not gone rusty?

Variables that interact

This experiment shows that oxygen and water on their own will not make iron rust. Terry and Tasha decided to set up another nail in a tube – this time just half full of plain water so that both oxygen and water are present. They left it for a week. This time they found that the nail started to rust.

Terry and Tasha showed that both oxygen and water are needed to make iron rust. Rusting only occurs when the two variables **interact**.

I'm going to put one nail in a tube of oil so that no oxygen or water can get in.

I will put a nail in water, but I will boil the water first to drive off any oxygen. I can compare this to your first tube that has no water or oxygen.

I'll put another nail in a tube of air. Oxygen will be there, but I'll put some silica gel in too, to make sure the air is dry.

I think my nail in water will go rusty.

I think that the nail in air with oxygen will rust.

	No oxygen	Oxygen present
no water	no rust	no rust
water present	no rust	rust present

Questions

1 Copy and complete each sentence by choosing from the words below:

will rust   will not rust

Iron in dry air _____.

Iron in water that is oxygen free _____.

Iron in water with oxygen _____.

2 Explain why:

a iron does not rust in the desert

b iron buried in swamps does not rust.

(*Hint*: oxygen gets used up when plants rot.)

3 Florida and Alaska both get plenty of rain, yet cars rust much faster in Florida than Alaska. Suggest another variable that might affect the speed at which iron rusts when both water and oxygen are present.

Alaska

North America

Florida

G1 Environmental chemistry

It's all around us

The land, air and sea make up our environment.

We live on the land. The rocks beneath us form the soil in which we grow our food.

The air we breathe is a mixture of gases. We'd soon die without the oxygen it contains.

Rivers carry rain water down to the sea. We need fresh water to drink.

Rocks and soil

You can't grow crops in rock. Plants need soil to grow. But most of the nutrients that plants need come from the rock. Soil forms when the rocks are physically and chemically weathered over tens or even hundreds of years. The chemicals in the rock react with water and air, making the nutrients.

Soils made from granite contain a lot of sand and clay. Many plants, such as heather, like this kind of soil and crops grow well in it. These soils are naturally slightly acidic. This acidity does not come from the damaging effects of acid rain pollution (see page 66).

Soils made from limestone or chalk have less sand and clay. They are often in thin layers, do not contain as many nutrients, and dry out very easily. Plants do not grow so well. These soils are naturally alkaline. Some plants love this, but heathers hate it!

Do you remember?

Weathering is when rocks break down. In physical weathering, the rocks are simply broken into smaller pieces. In chemical weathering, chemical reactions make new substances.

a The Scottish hillside in this photo below is covered in heather. Do you think the soil is acidic or alkaline?

Testing the soil

You can test soil to see if it is acidic or alkaline by shaking it with a little water and some universal indicator. Some flowers act as indicators, too. Hydrangeas have pink flowers when grown in alkaline soil, but blue flowers in acidic soil.

ⓑ **Fiona bought a beautiful blue hydrangea in Cornwall, but when she put it in her garden in London it turned pink. What happened?**

Looking after the air

About 50 years ago, most people in London heated their homes using open coal fires. The smoke and soot went up the chimney and got trapped in the autumn fog, forming thick smog. These days our city air **pollution** is caused by cars and lorries.

I can remember walking to school in the 1950s. Sometimes the smog was so thick that even in the day you couldn't see the people walking just in front of you. We called it a 'peasouper'. And all the soot and muck you breathed in … when you sneezed, your handkerchief turned black!

ⓒ **What fuel do most people use to heat their homes today?**

Looking after the water

We use water for drinking, washing, cooking and cleaning. We eat fish from the sea and enjoy seaside holidays. But we sometimes pollute our water resources. Around 150 years ago, all London's sewers flowed into the River Thames. In the summer, the MPs in the Houses of Parliament had to put up with the 'great stench' from the polluted river.

Today, sewage is carefully treated before the water goes back into rivers. Scientist take samples and monitor the pollution levels. If a company pollutes the river, they pay fines. Thanks to new laws and improved technology, fish have returned to the River Thames. Some people even swim in it!

Questions

1 Match the correct beginnings and endings of these sentences. Write them down.

Beginnings	Ends
Plants can't grow in rocks because …	… the chemicals in them react with air and water.
Rocks form soil when they are broken down and …	… soil is acidic.
Heather grows well in Scotland because …	… they can't get the nutrients they need from rock until it is weathered.

2 Why does London not get thick autumn smog these days?

3 Suggest two ways that show the River Thames is less polluted than it used to be.

For your notes:

- Soils form slowly as rocks are weathered physically and chemically.

- Soil is needed to grow plants.

- The land, air and sea can all suffer from **pollution**.

- Science can help to reduce pollution problems.

G2 Acid rain

What is acid rain?

All rain is naturally very slightly acidic because of the dissolved carbon dioxide in it. Over hundreds of years, all rain will chemically weather limestone rocks, statues and buildings. This is the word equation for the reaction.

carbon dioxide + water → carbonic acid

But other gases dissolve in rain to make it much more acidic – as acidic as the vinegar you put on your chips! This is called **acid rain**.

a **What problems do you think acid rain might cause?**

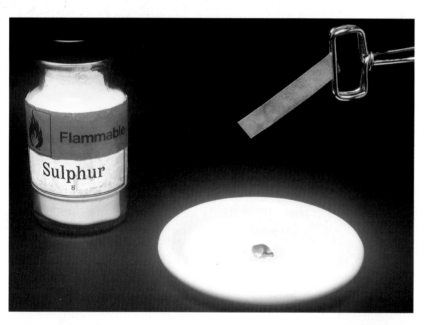

What causes the problem?

Sulphur is a yellow solid that burns in air to make a gas called sulphur dioxide.

sulphur + oxygen → sulphur dioxide

If sulphur dioxide gets into the air, it reacts with more oxygen and rain water to form a dilute solution of sulphuric acid.

b **Why is the damp pH paper in this photo turning red?**

Burning sulphur makes an acidic gas.

Where does it come from?

There is sulphur in volcanoes. Every time a volcano erupts, millions of tonnes of sulphur dioxide are sent up into the air. This causes a lot of acid rain. Lots more sulphur dioxide gets into the atmosphere during forest fires.

About half of all acid rain is caused naturally like this. There's not a lot we can do about these natural forms of air pollution.

Where do we come in?

There is also a lot of sulphur in fossil fuels such as coal, oil and gas. Sulphur dioxide is made when we burn fossil fuels. If it gets into the air, we get more acid rain. We burn millions of tonnes of fossil fuels every day. So we are responsible for making the problem of acid rain worse.

c **What fossil fuels were burned because of you today? (Think carefully.)**

Electricity is produced in power stations, which burn mainly fossil fuels. These produce millions of tonnes of sulphur dioxide over the years. Every time you use electricity, you are causing a little more air pollution.

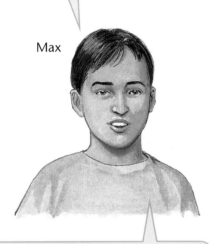

Max

Look at all this pollution we cause. We have to do something …

True, but we should still try to stop the pollution we do cause …

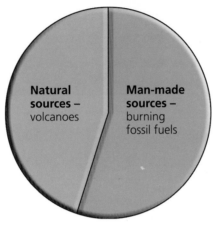

Natural sources – volcanoes

Man-made sources – burning fossil fuels

Global sources of acid rain.

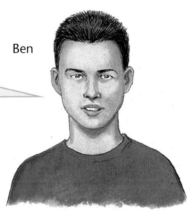

Ben

But look – as much acid rain is caused by volcanoes! What can we do about that?

d **Who do you agree with, and why?**

Questions

1 Copy and complete these sentences by choosing from the oxides in bold.

Normal rain is slightly acidic because of dissolved **carbon dioxide/sulphur dioxide**.

Acid rain is more acidic because of dissolved **carbon dioxide/sulphur dioxide**.

2 **a** Name one natural source of sulphur dioxide in the air.

 b Name one man-made source of sulphur dioxide in the air.

3 Most garages now sell 'low sulphur' petrol and diesel. Explain how this helps to reduce air pollution.

For your notes:

- Rain water is always slightly acidic.

- **Acid rain** is a much stronger acid. It forms when sulphur dioxide pollutes the air.

- Sulphur dioxide comes from natural sources such as volcanoes, and from burning fossil fuels.

Learn about:
- The effects of acid rain
- How to prevent and cure acid rain

G3 More about acid rain

So what's the problem?

Acid rain is corrosive. It makes iron bridges and machinery rust away even faster than usual. It also weathers limestone, which is a natural form of calcium carbonate. Many important buildings are built from limestone, such as Canterbury Cathedral. Acid rain has weakened them. Many wonderful sculptures and statues have also been ruined by acid rain.

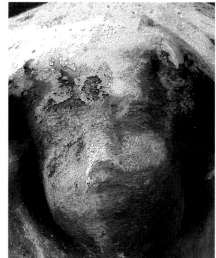
Exposed to acid rain.

Protected from acid rain.

(a) Copy and complete the word equation for the reaction of calcium carbonate with sulphuric acid in acid rain:

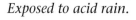

calcium carbonate + sulphuric acid → calcium sulphate + _____ + _____

(b) Suggest some building materials which will not be so badly affected by acid rain.

Is that all?

Damage to our buildings is a nuisance, but acid rain can cause really serious damage to the environment. Acid rain damages trees, like those in the photo on the right. If acid rain gets into rivers or lakes, it can also kill all the fish.

NORWAY

Not just a local problem

Power stations burning fossil fuels used to release millions of tonnes of sulphur dioxide into the air. The local area was badly affected by acid rain, so tall chimneys were added to carry away the gases in the wind. But the acid rain just fell somewhere else. Much of Britain's acid rain was blown to Norway.

(c) Why did the Norwegians blame Britain for the death of the fish in their rivers?

In the past, people just looked for local solutions to air pollution problems. Today we understand that that the problem is global. We have to work to reduce the pollution we cause, not just move it out of our area.

How can scientists help?

Some people blame scientists for the problems of pollution, but in fact scientists help solve the problems.

Scientists set up automatic datalogging stations all over the country, monitoring air and water pollution. Then they can find areas of bad pollution and work to reduce it. You can log on to these through the Internet and find out just how polluted your area is today.

d How do scientists use alkalis to reduce the effects of acid rain?

Power stations have to clean up their waste gases before releasing them. Scientists invented a way to spray the gases with a weak alkaline solution which neutralises the sulphur dioxide.

Some Scottish lakes lost their fish because of acid rain. Scientists neutralised the acid waters by adding lime (a soluble base, or alkali). New fish have now been put back into these lochs.

How can you help?

The more energy you use, the more pollution is made. We can all help to reduce pollution by changing the way we live.

- Use a little less energy at home by turning off lights or turning down the heating.

- Walk, cycle or take the bus instead of going by car.

Questions

1 Match the correct beginnings and endings of these sentences. Write them down.

Beginnings	Ends
An alkaline solution …	… kills fish in rivers and lakes.
Lime …	… neutralises the acid in lakes.
Limestone …	… is used to remove sulphur dioxide from power station waste gases.
Acid rain …	… is badly weathered by acid rain.

2 Design a poster to encourage people to think about what they can do to reduce pollution. Focus on changes they could make to their own lifestyle.

For your notes:

- Acid rain weathers limestone buildings, corrodes iron, and kills fish and trees.

- Scientists **monitor** pollution so they can do something if there is a problem.

- Power stations must now clean their waste gases using an alkaline solution.

- Lime is used to neutralise the effects of acid rain in lakes.

- We can all reduce pollution by making small changes to our lifestyles.

G4 Global warming

The trouble with burning petrol

Car exhaust contains some nasty and poisonous gases as well as sooty smoke. Walking or cycling along a busy street can be very unpleasant. Cars also produce lots of carbon dioxide. This is not poisonous, but it could still cause problems.

a Suggest another source of carbon dioxide in the air.

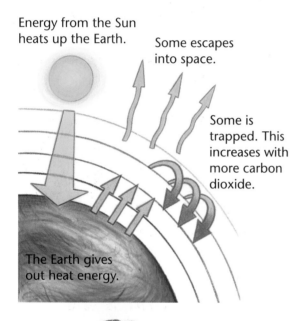

Energy from the Sun heats up the Earth.

Some escapes into space.

Some is trapped. This increases with more carbon dioxide.

The Earth gives out heat energy.

The greenhouse effect

Every day energy reaches the Earth from the Sun. But the Earth also radiates energy into space, so the Earth doesn't get too hot. The energy lost and energy gained are balanced, to give the Earth a stable temperature. Fortunately for us, this is suitable for living things. This balance is controlled by carbon dioxide in the air, which traps some of the heat energy. This is called the greenhouse effect.

All fossil fuels produce carbon dioxide when we burn them. We have burned so much of our fossil fuel reserves over the last 200 years that the amount of carbon dioxide in the air has gone up by a third. This extra carbon dioxide traps more energy, and so the Earth has started to warm up more. This is called **global warming**.

> *Carbon dioxide in the air causes global warming. It traps the Sun's energy and makes the Earth warm up. It's a disaster!*

> *How can carbon dioxide be a problem? We breathe it out, and plants need it to make their food. It's perfectly natural and can't possibly do any harm.*

> *Yes, some carbon dioxide is fine, but too much upsets the balance of gases in the air. We're burning our fossil fuels so fast that we're upsetting that balance!*

Petra

Sarah

b Who do you agree with, and why?

Does it matter?

Living in Britain, you might not think it much of a problem if the Earth warmed up a bit. But things are not that simple. Making the Earth hotter would change the environment.

Some of the ice at the North and South Poles will melt, so the size of the oceans will increase. The sea level will rise and some land will be flooded.

In other areas it will get hotter and the rains will dry up. Crops will die as the land turns to desert, and millions of people could starve.

With more energy in the air, the weather will become more violent and unpredictable. There will be high winds and heavy rains in some areas.

c Who do you think is more likely to suffer from the effects of global warming, people in the developed or developing world? Explain your answer.

What can we do?

The more energy resources we use, the more pollution we make. It's almost as simple as that. So anything we do to save energy can help.

In 1997, leaders of the world's developed countries agreed in the Kyoto Agreement to cut the amount of carbon dioxide they produce by 6%. Unfortunately, most governments aren't doing this yet and the USA has not made a start.

d Write a letter to the President of the United States of America explaining why he should try to make the Kyoto Agreement work.

Questions

1 Match the correct beginnings and endings of these sentences. Write them down.

Beginnings	Ends
Carbon dioxide ...	... could occur if global warming starts to melt the ice at the poles, or change weather patterns.
The greenhouse effect ...	... is produced when fossil fuels burn.
Flooding and droughts ...	... happens if extra carbon dioxide in the air increases the greenhouse effect.
Global warming ...	... is caused by carbon dioxide in the air trapping some of the heat energy radiated by the Earth.

2 In Athens you can drive your car for only four days a week.

   a How does this help to decrease air pollution?

   b Do you think it is a good idea?

3 What do you think might happen to the temperature of the Earth if there was a lot *less* carbon dioxide in the air? Make a list of the problems this might cause.

For your notes:

- Car exhaust contains a mixture of polluting gases.

- Burning fossil fuels makes carbon dioxide.

- More carbon dioxide in the air increases the greenhouse effect and may cause **global warming**.

More about global warming

Henry and Leena are studying global warming. They know that many people think that we are responsible for global warming because of burning fossil fuels. They want to look at evidence for the link between carbon dioxide in the air and the temperature of the Earth.

They found some data on the Internet that gave the percentage of carbon dioxide in the air, and how the global temperature has changed over the 40 years up to the year 2000. They decided to plot graphs of these figures and compare them, to see if there was a pattern.

Here is the graph they made from the data. They talked about the patterns in the graph.

The carbon dioxide level and the mean annual temperature have both gone up.

Perhaps. But the temperature graph is not very clear, is it? The trend goes up, but it jumps about a lot.

That's true. And now I look more closely, it seems to have cooled off in the mid-1960s before getting warmer again.

(a) **Do you think there is an obvious pattern in the graph?**

This graph above does show a general trend of temperature rising with carbon dioxide levels. But Henry has pointed out that some of the points in the 1960s do not fit the trend quite so well. A point that doesn't fit the trend is called an **anomaly**. Anomalies need further investigation.

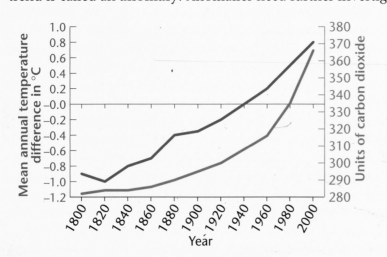

Going further back in time ...

Henry and Leena decide that they need more evidence. They want to know if the warmer period in the early 1960s was a simple anomaly or part of a wider pattern. They find this graph that looks back 200 years. We have been burning fossil fuels for the last 200 years. It shows five times as much data, which gives stronger evidence.

(b) **What is the overall trend in this graph?**

(c) **Does the drop in temperature in the 1960s look like an anomaly or part of a pattern?**

... and even further

Henry finds a graph showing just temperature for the last 1000 years.

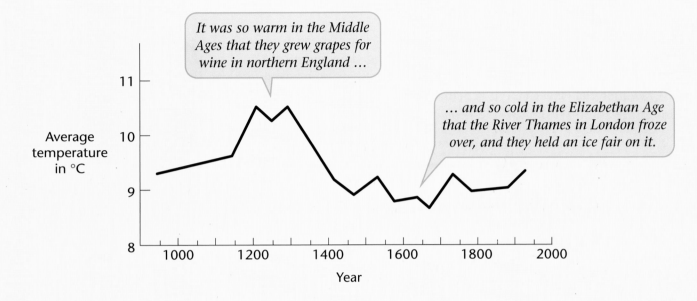

> It was so warm in the Middle Ages that they grew grapes for wine in northern England ...

> ... and so cold in the Elizabethan Age that the River Thames in London froze over, and they held an ice fair on it.

... and don't forget the ice ages

Then Leena remembers reading about the ice ages. Around 20000 years ago, Britain was covered by ice and woolly mammoths roamed the country. So much water was frozen in icebergs that the sea level fell and what is now the English Channel was dry land.

Leena and Henry realise that the Earth's climate is much more complicated than they thought. It could warm up, melt the ice and flood the land – or we could have another ice age. The role of carbon dioxide is not clear. The amount does seem to vary naturally. But we have upset the balance by burning fossil fuels, which is probably not a good idea.

d Scientists think that carbon dioxide levels during the Middle Ages and Elizabethan times stayed fairly constant. Does that fit the pattern of the last 200 years?

Questions

1 Copy and complete these sentences by choosing from the words in bold.

a Over the last 200 years, the average temperature of the Earth has risen by just under **0.2°/2°/10°/20°** Celsius.

b The amount of **oxygen/carbon dioxide/nitrogen** in the air has also gone up because we have burned fossil fuels.

c This suggests that the two are linked, but does not prove that burning fossil fuels causes **ice ages/global warming/woolly mammoths**.

2 a Plot your own line graphs from these figures for the last 120 years.

b Describe the pattern each graph shows and compare the two trends.

Year	1880	1900	1920	1940	1960	1980	2000
Carbon dioxide level	290	296	302	310	321	340	370
Average temperature difference in °C	–0.45	–0.4	–0.2	0	0.05	0.3	0.5

H1 Products from reactions

Particles 2

Using chemistry

Some useful products

Some chemical reactions make useful products. Nearly everything we use has been made from **raw materials** changed by chemical reactions into something more useful. Bricks are made by heating the raw material clay. Cement is made by heating the raw material limestone and reacting it with a little clay.

Think about the materials used in a car.

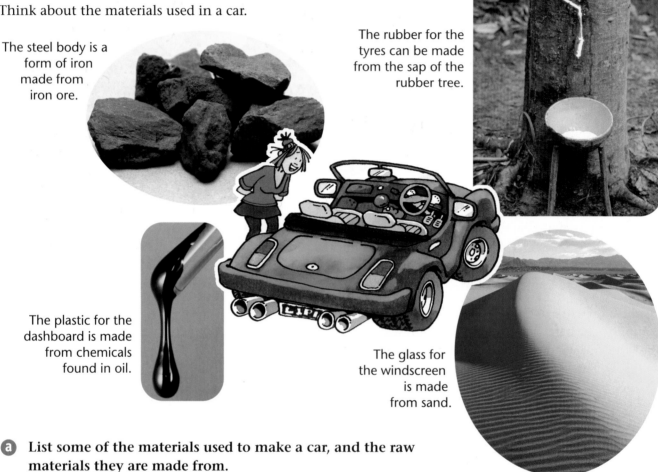

The steel body is a form of iron made from iron ore.

The rubber for the tyres can be made from the sap of the rubber tree.

The plastic for the dashboard is made from chemicals found in oil.

The glass for the windscreen is made from sand.

a List some of the materials used to make a car, and the raw materials they are made from.

PURE CARBON
BIT OF CARBON
SUGAR
BIT OF SUGAR
STARCH

The chemistry of food

When you cook food, chemical reactions take place. They break down food to make it softer, or easier to digest. They also make it taste better. When you make toast, some of the starch in the bread is broken down into sugar, which makes toast taste sweet. But burnt toast is just carbon! (Water is also produced in these reactions.)

b Copy and complete these word equations.

    (i)   for making toast ...   starch → _____ + water

    (ii) for burning toast ...   starch → _____ + water

When food goes bad, the chemical reactions are not so useful. Bacteria and fungi grow on the food. The chemicals they make are poisonous waste products. If you eat food that has 'gone off', these poisons can make you very ill.

But sometimes we use fungi to make special food for us, using the chemical reactions going on inside them. Quorn is a protein that can be used as a cheap alternative to meat. It is made by growing special fungi on starch from potatoes. Other chemical reactions are then used to make it look and taste like chicken or beef.

c Which group of people might want to eat Quorn rather than meat?

The chemistry of life

All life relies on chemical reactions.

● Plants make the food they need using a chemical reaction. They use sunlight to combine carbon dioxide and water to make glucose. Oxygen is a waste product.

● All living things respire. Glucose combines with the oxygen you breathe, and makes carbon dioxide and water as waste products. This chemical reaction gives out energy and is similar to burning a fuel (see page 76).

● Chemical reactions during digestion make glucose from starchy foods such as bread. The glucose is used for respiration.

d You breathe in oxygen but breathe out carbon dioxide. Where does the carbon dioxide come from?

Do you remember?

Plants and animals get the energy they need from their food, using the chemical reaction called respiration.

Questions

1 Here is a list of things used to build a house, and a list of raw materials used to make them. Match the correct raw material to each product. One has been done for you.

Products	Raw materials
brick	sand
cement	gypsum
wallpaper	limestone
plaster	clay
glass	wood

2 Iron is made from iron ore (iron oxide) by heating iron ore with carbon.

   a What is the useful product of this reaction?

   b What is the other product likely to be?

   c Write a word equation for this reaction.

3 List three chemical reactions that go on in living things.

For your notes:

● Most materials around us are made from **raw materials** by chemical reactions.

● Many chemical reactions are useful to us.

Getting energy

Thermal (heat) energy is often given out during chemical reactions. Combustion reactions give out thermal and light energy, which is why they are so useful to us. Displacement reactions give out thermal energy too. When you add zinc to a test tube of copper sulphate solution, you will feel it warm up.

Fuels and combustion

Fuels contain stored chemical energy. This is released when they burn. Combustion is the chemical reaction of a fuel with oxygen in the air. For fuels, the energy released is more important than the new chemical products.

fuel + oxygen $\xrightarrow{\text{combustion}}$ waste gases

energy is released

a List three things that can act as fuel in a house fire.

A combustion reaction out of control.

Burning fossil fuels

Most people in Britain get energy for their homes from fossil fuels: coal, oil or gas. Even if your home is 'all electric', coal is burned in many power stations to generate the electricity. Coal contains carbon. When it burns it produces carbon dioxide.

carbon + oxygen → carbon dioxide

energy is released

Do you remember?

Fossil fuels were made from the remains of plants or animals. The plants originally got their stored energy from the Sun.

b What problem is caused for the Earth by burning too much coal?

Natural gas is a form of fossil sunshine.

Oil and gas are made from compounds of carbon and hydrogen called **hydrocarbons**. When they burn in oxygen, the carbon makes carbon dioxide and the hydrogen makes water. For example, natural gas contains a hydrocarbon called methane which burns in oxygen like this:

methane + oxygen → carbon dioxide + water

energy is released

c Jane says all cars are powered by the Sun. Is she right?

Car exhaust gas contains carbon dioxide and water, as you might expect, but also some deadly poisonous carbon monoxide. Carbon monoxide is produced when there is not enough oxygen to react with the fuel. If you breathe it in it stops your blood carrying oxygen and could kill you.

Alternative fuels

There's one big problem with fossil fuels. They are going to run out, even if we try to conserve them to make them last longer. We need to find alternative fuels.

In Brazil, where there is little fossil fuel but lots of sugar cane, cars run on ethanol instead of petrol. The ethanol is made from sugar.

d Copy and complete this word equation for the burning of ethanol.

> ethanol + _____ → carbon dioxide + water

The space shuttle burns hydrogen in its main engines.

main engines

Hydrogen – the fuel for the future?

Hydrogen may be an alternative fuel for the future. It is a very clean fuel because it makes just water and nothing else when it burns. But hydrogen is a gas, which takes up a lot of space, so it has to be compressed to a liquid in a very strong container. Also, hydrogen can explode when it is mixed with oxygen.

e Copy and complete this word equation for the burning of hydrogen.

> hydrogen + oxygen → _____

f Why is hydrogen a cleaner fuel than ethanol?

Questions

1 Match the correct beginnings and endings of these sentences. Write them down.

Beginnings	Ends
When petrol burns in a car engine it transfers its energy as …	… heat and some light energy.
Fossil fuels store energy as …	… movement energy and heat energy.
When fuels burn the energy is released as …	… chemical energy.

2 When wood burns in oxygen it forms carbon dioxide and water. Which two elements must it contain?

3 In California some buses run on hydrogen fuel. Suggest:

a one possible reason for doing this

b one possible problem they have had to overcome.

For your notes:

- Coal makes carbon dioxide when it burns.

- **Hydrocarbons** make carbon dioxide and water when they burn.

- Hydrogen is a 'pollution free' fuel as it produces only water when it burns.

H3 Reactions in balance

Particles 2

Making a compound

Kerry and Nathan made iron sulphide by heating iron filings and sulphur in a test tube. They talked about how much iron sulphide had been made.

ⓐ **Who do you agree with, Kerry or Nathan?**

Do you remember?

The mass of a solution is the same as the mass of the solute and solvent together.

We reacted 2g of iron with 1g of sulphur.

I can't see any yellow sulphur left, so the mass must have gone down.

I don't think anything came out of the tube when it reacted.

No, the sulphur's now in the compound – I bet its mass is 3g.

Rearranging atoms

The reactants are iron atoms and sulphur atoms. The product iron sulphide contains both iron and sulphur atoms combined. Each iron atom is next to sulphur atoms, and each sulphur atom is next to iron atoms.

The total number of atoms in the reactants and the product is the same. They are just rearranged into a compound.

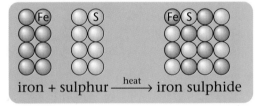

iron + sulphur $\xrightarrow{\text{heat}}$ iron sulphide

The mass stays the same

In all chemical reactions, the total number of atoms involved stays the same. So the total mass stays the same – we say that mass is **conserved**.

These two photos show hydrochloric acid neutralising sodium hydroxide. The products are sodium chloride (common salt) and water.

Before (left) and after (right) mixing.

ⓑ **Explain why both balances in these photos show the same reading.**

Here is a word equation for this reaction. Below the names of the compounds are their formulae.

hydrochloric acid + sodium hydroxide → sodium chloride + water
HCl   NaOH   NaCl H_2O

c How many of each type of atom are there in water? How do you know?

d List each kind of atom on each side of the equation.

Look at the picture of the balance. The number of hydrogen, chlorine, sodium and oxygen atoms in the reactants (left) is the same as the number of atoms in the products (right). The total number of atoms stays the same in all chemical reactions. This is why mass is conserved.

$HCl + NaOH \longrightarrow NaCl + H_2O$

The number of atoms is the same on each side.

Writing word equations

Word equations show what is happening during a chemical reaction. You need to know the reactants you are starting with and the products you end up with.

For example, ethanol burns in oxygen to give carbon dioxide and water. In this reaction, the reactants are ethanol and oxygen. The products are carbon dioxide and water.

You can write any other information about the reaction over the arrow. For this reaction you can write 'combustion'.

ethanol + oxygen $\xrightarrow{\text{combustion}}$ carbon dioxide + water

For heating iron with sulphur you can write 'heating'.

iron + sulphur $\xrightarrow{\text{heating}}$ iron sulphide

Questions

1 Copy and complete the sentences, choosing from the words in bold.

In a chemical reaction the **molecules/atoms** are rearranged and combine in a different way. The number of **compounds/atoms** stays the same in the reaction, so the mass is **conserved/transferred**.

2 Write word equations for these reactions.
 a The iron filings on a sparkler burn in oxygen in the air to give iron oxide.
 b Carbon reacts with iron oxide to give carbon dioxide and iron metal.
 c Magnesium reacts with hydrochloric acid to give hydrogen and magnesium chloride.

3 When you heat magnesium ribbon in air it burns to give white magnesium oxide.
 a Write a word equation for this reaction.
 b 2.4 g of magnesium formed 4 g of magnesium oxide. What mass of oxygen must have combined with the magnesium?

For your notes:

- In a chemical reaction, mass is **conserved** because the total number of atoms stays the same.

- In a chemical reaction, the atoms are rearranged to make new compounds.

H4 The story of burning

Think about:
- What happens when things burn …
- … and how we found out.

Phlogiston rules!

Today, we know that when something burns, it reacts with the oxygen in the air. How was this discovered?

When wood burns you are left with ash – a lot less ash than the wood you started with. About 300 years ago, a scientist called George Stahl came up with the idea of **phlogiston** to explain burning.

> *Something must be leaving the fuel as it burns. I'll call it phlogiston.*

> *So things that burn must contain phlogiston. When they burn they split apart and phlogiston is released.*

You can show this idea by writing:

fuel → ash + phlogiston (in the flames)

The idea of phlogiston was very popular. Most scientists used it to explain burning.

ⓐ How does the idea that something is lost on burning compare with what we know today?

A new discovery

In 1774, Joseph Priestley did an experiment heating a substance called red calx. Mercury was made, as he expected. But he was surprised that a gas was also made.

Priestley was even more surprised when he found that this new gas made a candle burn more brightly.

ⓑ What do you think this gas might be?

An alternative idea

A year or so later, Antoine Lavoisier decided to reverse Priestley's experiment. He burned mercury to see what happened.

Lavoisier did his burning experiment very carefully. He trapped the mercury and the air in a special flask, with its end dipped into a bowl of liquid mercury.

Lavoisier heated the mercury in the flask. A red substance that looked like red calx was made on its surface. He also noticed that some of the mercury in the bowl was sucked into the flask. This meant the amount of air in the flask had decreased! Something had *left* the air and joined with the mercury.

Lavoisier had something *joining* during burning. Stahl and Priestley had something (phlogiston, or gas) *leaving* during burning.

c **Which idea matches what we know today?**

Lavoisier realised that the gas taken out of the air in his experiment must be the same as Priestley's 'new gas'. He named this gas oxygen. Then he showed that oxygen was involved in burning. When substances burn they join with oxygen from the air.

A modern explanation

When mercury is heated in air, mercury atoms combine with oxygen atoms in the air to form a compound called mercury oxide. Mercury oxide is the scientific name for the substance once called red calx. You can write word equations for Lavoisier's and Priestley's experiments:

mercury + oxygen → mercury oxide

mercury oxide → mercury + oxygen

Lavoisier did lots of experiments and showed that the mass of something burning goes up, not down. This proved that the phlogiston idea was wrong. Eventually all scientists agreed with Lavoisier and his 'new idea' about oxygen became the accepted theory.

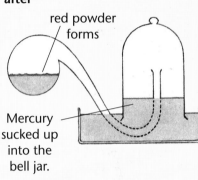

Lavoisier's experiment.

Questions

1 Tony tried a modern version of Lavoisier's experiment. He put a crucible, on top of a heatproof mat, on an electronic balance connected to his computer. He used datalogging to take a mass reading every second. He put a coil of magnesium ribbon into the crucible and lit it. Look at this graph of his results.

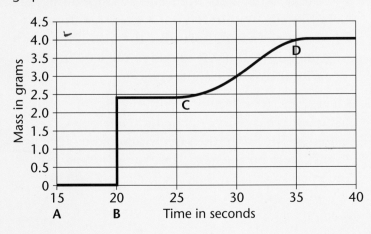

a Match each of these sentences to one of the letters on the chart:

   (i) The magnesium stopped burning.

   (ii) The datalogging programme started to run.

   (iii) The magnesium started to burn.

   (iv) The magnesium ribbon was put in the crucible.

b Did the mass go up or down as the magnesium reacted?

c Did Tony's experiment support Lavoisier's idea or Priestley's phlogiston theory?

Learn about:
● Energy transfers involving electricity
● Conservation of energy

I1 Make it work

On the move

Ellen's MP3 player works because of electricity. The batteries inside give the MP3 player electrical energy. Batteries are a convenient source of electrical energy.

$$\text{electrical energy} \longrightarrow \text{MP3 player} \longrightarrow \text{sound energy}$$

Look at this energy transfer diagram below. The microwave oven is plugged in. It needs electrical energy to work, and it gets this from the mains.

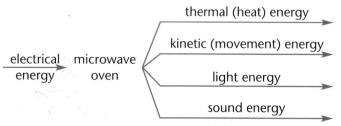

thermal (heat) energy

kinetic (movement) energy

electrical energy → microwave oven

light energy

sound energy

ⓐ Look at the energy transfer diagram for the microwave oven. Write down the types of energy being given out by the microwave oven.

In and out of storage

This photo is from Ellen's skiing holiday.

Look at the energy transfer diagram below for the ski lift. It transfers energy from electricity to the skiers. The skiers end up with a store of gravitational energy. They then use this stored energy to ski down the slope.

electrical energy → | gravitational energy in the skiers |

ⓑ Some ski lifts get their energy from diesel motors (like the ones in lorries). Others get their energy from electric motors (like the one in a washing machine). What is the advantage of an electric motor over a diesel motor?

Ellen reads about two different torches. One torch has batteries. It has a store of chemical energy in the batteries. The other torch is a wind-up torch like the one in the photo on the next page. You wind the handle and the torch stores energy as strain energy.

Did you know?

Gravitational energy is also called **gravitational potential energy.**

When you switch the torch on, the electricity carries the energy between the store and the lamp, making it work.

Look at the energy transfer diagram below right for the wind-up torch.

c Draw your own energy transfer diagram for the battery torch.

Place to place

Electricity is a great way of moving energy around. Think about an electric heater and a fire. They do the same job, but the fire is smellier, dirtier, noisier and more dangerous. It also takes a long time to make a fire and to clean it up afterwards. It only takes a second to switch the electric heater on and off.

d Compare a candle to an electric lamp. Why is the lamp a better source of light energy?

We take electricity for granted, but the energy it carries has to come from somewhere. Energy can be stored, or moved about, but it cannot be made. We say that energy is **conserved**.

The energy carried by the electricity we use in our homes comes from power stations. The power stations get the energy from coal or the wind or another energy resource.

strain energy in the spring	electrical energy →

Do you remember?

Energy is measured in joules, J. There are 1000 joules in one kilojoule, kJ.

Questions

1 Copy and complete the table. Choose from these three devices for the first column.

     mobile phone   iron   food mixer

Device	Energy from ...	Energy in as ...	Energy out as ...
	batteries	electrical energy	_____ energy, _____ energy and _____ energy
	the mains	electrical energy	_____ energy
	the mains	electrical energy	_____ energy, _____ energy and _____ energy

2 Think about a hairdryer. 750 J of electrical energy goes into the hairdryer. 5 J of sound energy and 10 J of kinetic energy come out of the hairdryer. The hairdryer also gives out heat (thermal) energy.
  a Energy is conserved. How much energy must the hairdryer give out?
  b How much energy does the hairdryer give out as sound energy and kinetic energy combined?
  c How much energy does the hairdryer give out as thermal energy?
  d Draw an energy transfer diagram for the hairdryer. Use the one for the microwave oven on page 82 to help you.

3 Imagine life without electricity. What would you have to do differently in the time between getting up and arriving at school?

For your notes:

- Energy is transferred as electrical energy, sound energy, light energy, heat (thermal) energy or kinetic energy.

- Energy is stored as chemical energy, gravitational energy or strain energy.

- Electricity is a clean and convenient way of transferring energy.

- Energy is **conserved**.

I2 Energy in and out

Circuits

We can use Ellen on her skiing holiday as a model of an electric circuit.

Do you remember?

Electrical devices need a complete circuit to work.

The flow of the skiers in the diagram shows the current. Energy is put into the circuit at the ski lift, where the skiers are lifted up. Energy comes out of the circuit at the ski run, as the skiers zoom down the slope. The ski lift is like the cell, putting energy into the circuit. The ski run is like the lamp, where the energy comes out of the circuit.

a **What in the model shows:**
(i) the cell?
(ii) the current?
(iii) the lamp?

Do you remember?

Two or more cells together make a battery. Cells put electrical energy into the circuit.

Voltage

This photo below shows a cell. Inside the cell there are substances that are a store of chemical energy. When you put the cell into a circuit, the substances react and give out electrical energy.

If you look at a cell, you will see a voltage written on it. The cell in the photo is 1.5 V. Voltage is measured in volts, or V for short. We measure voltage with a **voltmeter**. The circuit symbol for a voltmeter is Ⓥ.

Mel and Jeff are measuring the voltage across four parts of a circuit. A drawing of their experiment is shown opposite, with the circuit diagram next to it. The voltmeter is not in the circuit. It is in a separate loop. To measure voltage you connect the voltmeter *across* the battery or *across* the lamp.

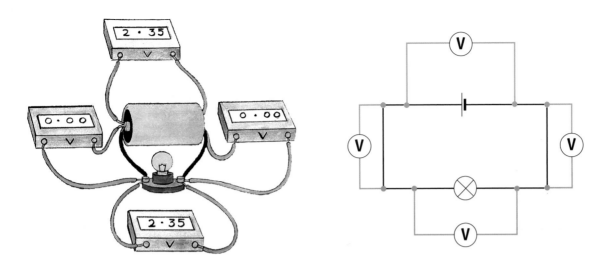

The black wires show the circuit. The wires going to the voltmeters are pink.

Voltage tells us where there is a change in energy in the circuit. There is a voltage across the cell: this is where energy is put in. There is a voltage across the lamp: this is where the energy leaves.

Modelling voltage

Where does voltage fit into our model of the circuit?

Look back at the model on page 84. The skiers at the bottom have less energy because they are lower down. The skiers at the top have more energy because they have been lifted up. The voltage is the change in height.

There is a big height change over the ski lift part of the circuit. This shows the voltage across the cell.

There is a big height change when the skiers go down the ski run. This shows the voltage across the lamp.

There is no height change when the skiers walk along at the top and the bottom. This shows that there is no voltage across the wires.

b What is the voltage across:
(i) the cell?
(ii) the lamp?
(iii) each wire?

c Why is there no voltage across the wires?

d Ellen decides to go up the first chair lift, and then up a second chair lift. That means she can ski down two separate ski runs before she reaches the bottom.
(i) How many 'cells' are there in this model?
(ii) How many lamps are in this model?
(iii) Draw a circuit diagram of the circuit that fits with this model.

Questions

1 Explain what these words or symbols mean:

voltage   volts   (V)   V

2 Sort out each jumble of words to make correct sentences about voltage.

a volts in measured is voltage

b is a measured voltage voltmeter using

c lamp voltage brighter more the the the the

For your notes:

● Voltage is measured across parts of a circuit, using a **voltmeter**.

● There is a voltage across any part of the circuit where energy is coming in or going out.

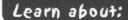

I3 Using electricity

High voltage

Look at the photo of lightning below. The voltage between the cloud and the ground is 300 000 V. That means a lot of energy is being transferred between the cloud and the ground.

Fast-moving electric trains have lots of kinetic energy. The overhead cables in the photo (above right) have a voltage of 25 000 V across them. The mains cables coming into our homes have a voltage of 230 V across them. This voltage is enough to give us the electrical energy we need. The larger the voltage, the more energy we can get from the circuit.

a Why can't you run electric trains on a 230 V mains supply?

Did you know?

Electricity kills about 30 people a year in UK homes and injures about 2000 others. Treat it with respect: never handle electrical devices with wet hands, keep them away from water, and always use a qualified electrician to do repairs.

Paying for energy

The electricity meter in your home measures the amount of energy you transfer from the mains. You pay the electricity supplier for the energy.

Look at this table. It shows the amount of energy transferred every second by different electrical devices in your home.

Electrical device	Energy transferred every second, in joules
100 W light bulb	100
60 W light bulb	60
electric cooker	132 000
microwave oven	850
washing machine	1200
tumble dryer	5800

b Why is it cheaper to use a microwave oven than an electric cooker to heat food?

Wasting energy

Think about a washing machine. You want the drum where you put the washing to turn, and the water to go in and out. You don't want the air around the washing machine warming up, or the washing machine making a lot of noise. But this can happen and some of the energy that goes into the washing machine is wasted.

Look at the labels on the two washing machines in this photo. One washing machine has a high 'A' grade for **energy efficiency**. The other washing machine has only a 'B' grade. Devices with a high energy efficiency waste less energy. The 'A' grade washing machine wastes less energy. More of the energy ends up where you want it to go.

When energy ends up in the wrong places, we say it is **dissipated**. Devices with low energy efficiencies dissipate a lot of energy to the surroundings.

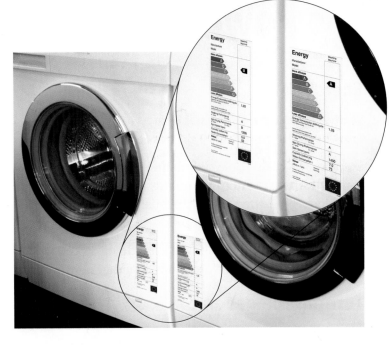

C You also need to use your washing machine in an energy-saving way. Explain why using a 40°C wash rather than a 60°C wash saves energy.

Saving energy

We can save energy and reduce our electricity bills.

Turn things off when you aren't using them. Don't leave TVs and computers on standby because that still wastes energy.

Always buy things with a good energy efficiency. That includes light bulbs.

Make sure you insulate your home. If you let the thermal energy escape you have to pay for more energy to replace it.

It isn't just about money. We don't have unlimited energy resources and we shouldn't be throwing energy away.

Questions

1 Our mains supply is 230V. Why don't we have a safer, lower voltage coming into our homes, like 50V?

2 Use the information in the table on the opposite page to explain why doing these things saves energy:

  a turning off lights when they are not needed

  b changing 100W bulbs to 60W bulbs

  c hanging out the washing rather than using the tumble dryer.

3 Helen wants her mother to buy a more energy-efficient washing machine. The more energy-efficient washing machine costs £65 more. Explain how the more expensive washing machine could save Helen's mother money.

For your notes:

- The higher the voltage, the more energy can be transferred.

- Different devices transfer different amounts of energy from a circuit.

- We pay for electrical energy, so using less electricity saves money and energy.

- Some devices have high **energy efficiencies**. They **dissipate** less energy to the surroundings.

I4 Power stations

Energy in

We use electricity to transfer energy into our homes. How does the energy get into the electricity?

Look at this bike. It has a dynamo. The dynamo transfers energy from the moving wheel into electricity. This then lights the bike lights. A dynamo takes in kinetic energy and produces electrical energy.

The electricity we use at home is made in power stations that have huge dynamos called **generators**.

Turning the generator

On a bike, the dynamo is spun by the bike wheel to make electricity. The power station generator also has to spin to produce electricity. Generators are spun by a **turbine**. Most generators are spun by a steam turbine. Water is heated until it boils. The steam is then used to turn the turbine. A model steam turbine is shown in the photo on the right.

The water can be heated in many different ways. Many power stations in Britain burn natural gas to heat the water. Others burn coal or oil. In hot, sunny countries the water can be heated to boiling by the Sun.

A power station's generator.

chemical energy in the fossil fuel → thermal energy → water → kinetic energy → turbine → kinetic energy → generator → electrical energy

(a) **Draw your own energy transfer diagram for a power station that uses solar power.**

Do you remember?

Turbines can also be turned by the wind, by falling water and by waves. Electricity made by falling water is called hydroelectric power.

The best way

Mary's class is discussing the advantages and disadvantages of different ways of generating electricity.

Mary's group is concentrating on the environmental damage.

ⓑ Read what Mary, Jim and Lucy have to say. Give your opinion about which way of generating electricity causes:
(i) the least environmental damage
(ii) the most environmental damage.

When you burn fossil fuels, you make a lot of waste gases. The carbon dioxide causes global warming. The sulphur dioxide causes acid rain.

Lots of wind turbines are ugly and noisy.

To get falling water you need to build dams. That makes new lakes and changes the way rivers flow. Lots of animals and plants lose their habitats.

Mary

Jim

Lucy

Peter's group is concentrating on how to make sure we have enough electricity in the future.

ⓒ Do you agree with Sue? Give your reasons.

Solar energy, wind, waves and falling water are all renewable energy sources. We should use them.

John

But it costs so much money to build wind turbines and hydroelectric power stations. We can't use solar power in Britain because of the weather.

Peter

Fossil fuels will run out soon. They are non-renewable.

Kate

Sue

We will have to use fossil fuels until they run out. We can worry about it then.

Questions

1 Write out each word along with its correct scientific meaning.

Words	Scientific meanings
conserved	makes things work
dissipated	not used up, just transferred or stored
efficiency	spread about to the surroundings
energy	the fraction of the energy that ends up where you want it
generator	being used up faster than it can be replaced
non-renewable	being replaced, usually by the Sun
renewable	changes kinetic energy into electrical energy
turbine	transfers kinetic energy to the generator

2 The list below shows four energy resources used in power stations. Use the information on this page and anything else you know to come up with one advantage and one disadvantage for each. You can use the same advantage or disadvantage more than once.

wind   coal   solar   falling water

For your notes:

- **Generators** transfer energy to electricity.

- **Turbines** transfer kinetic energy to generators.

- Turbines can be turned by steam, wind, falling water and waves.

- The steam is often made by burning fossil fuels. The waste gases from this cause global warming and acid rain.

- Fossil fuels are non-renewable. Solar power, wind, waves and falling water are renewable.

J1 A massive problem

Learn about:

● Mass, distance and gravitational attraction

Attracting bodies

It's hard to believe but things with mass are attracted to other things with mass. The more mass the things have, the more they are attracted. You are attracted to the Earth and the Earth is also attracted to you!

There's an attraction between us.

You wish!

Don't worry, he finds the ground 15 billion times more attractive.

Do you remember?

Gravitational attraction is the force that pulls an object towards the Earth. We feel gravitational attraction as weight. On Earth, 1 kg of mass has a weight of 10 N.

On the Moon

Sharon has a mass of 66 kg. There is a gravitational attraction of 660 N pulling Sharon towards the centre of the Earth. This is Sharon's weight.

If Sharon stood on the Moon, she would have the same mass but a different weight. The Moon has a smaller mass than the Earth. The gravitational attraction between Sharon and the Moon would be less than on Earth, only 110 N. Her weight on the Moon is one-sixth of her weight on Earth.

On the Moon, 1 kg of mass has a weight of 1.7 N, compared with a weight of 10 N on Earth.

ⓐ **What would be Sharon's mass on the Moon?**

on Earth
weight 660 N
mass 66 kg

on Moon
weight 110 N
mass 66 kg

On planets

Different planets have different gravitational attraction because they have different masses. Some have a larger mass than the Earth and some have a smaller mass.

Mars has a smaller mass than Earth. On Mars, 1 kg of mass has a weight of 4 N. Jupiter has a much larger mass than Earth. On Jupiter, 1 kg of mass has a weight of 26 N.

ⓑ **Where would Sharon have the largest weight, Mercury, Earth or Jupiter?**

The Sun is the biggest object in our Solar System, with the biggest mass. The gravitational attraction between the Sun and the planets keeps the Solar System together.

Do you remember?

The Solar System has the Sun at its centre. Nine planets orbit the Sun.

Distances apart

Mars has twice the mass of Mercury. You would expect the Sun to attract Mars more than it attracts Mercury, but it doesn't.

The gravitational attraction between the Sun and Mercury is 10 times bigger than the gravitational attraction between the Sun and Mars. This is because Mercury is much closer to the Sun than Mars is. Mars is four times further away, so the gravitational attraction is much less.

Gravitational attraction depends on the distance between the two objects as well as the mass. The bigger the distance between the two objects, the weaker the gravitational attraction.

c **Planet A and planet B orbit the same star. They both have the same mass. Planet A is 20 million km from the star. Planet B is 40 million km from the star. Which planet will be pulled towards the star with the larger gravitational attraction? Why?**

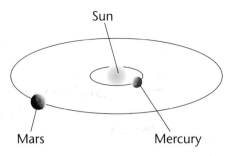

Escaping the Earth

Think about what happens when you jump. You push against the Earth and you move upwards, but the gravitational attraction of the Earth is always pulling you back down. To keep going upwards, you would have to keep pushing.

That's what rockets do. They produce a steady **thrust** or pushing force. To start moving upwards, the thrust has to be greater than the weight of the rocket.

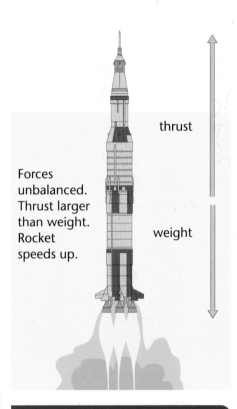

thrust

Forces unbalanced. Thrust larger than weight. Rocket speeds up.

weight

Questions

1 Decide whether these statements are true or false.

   a Large masses attract small masses, but small masses don't attract large masses.

   b The larger the mass of an object, the more it attracts other objects that have mass.

   c You would weigh more on Jupiter than on Earth.

   d Your mass is less on the Moon.

2 The Saturn V rocket had a mass of 3 000 000 kg.

   a What was the weight of the rocket when it was on Earth?

   b The lift-off thrust was 35 000 000 N. Explain why the rocket moved upwards.

3 How does gravitational attraction between two objects change with:

   a the mass of the objects?

   b the distance between them?

For your notes:

- Gravitational attraction depends on the mass of the two objects attracting each other. It is different on other planets and on the Moon.

- Gravitational attraction also depends on the distance between the two objects. The larger the distance, the weaker the attraction.

- To escape from the Earth, rockets need to push with a **thrust** greater than their weight.

J2 Satellites

Sputnik

A **satellite** is an object that orbits a larger object. In 1957 Sputnik 1 orbited the Earth for 52 days. It was the first **artificial satellite**, a satellite made by people.

a **What is an artificial satellite?**

Did you know?

The word 'sputnik' means travelling companion in Russian.

Sputnik 1 had a mass of 83.6 kg and a diameter of 58 cm.

Natural satellites

The Earth is a satellite of the Sun and the Moon is a satellite of Earth. They are **natural satellites**. In general, moons are satellites of planets and planets are satellites of stars.

b **Name a satellite of the Sun other than the Earth.**

Staying in orbit

Sputnik 1 fell back to Earth after 52 days. This was because it started to slow down. To stay in orbit, satellites have to be moving fast.

Look at this drawing of the girl with the ball and string. The tension in the string is pulling the ball inwards. The ball doesn't move inwards because it is travelling so fast.

In the same way, Sputnik 1 was pulled inwards by the gravitational attraction between it and the Earth. While it was travelling quickly, it stayed in orbit. When it slowed down, it fell to Earth.

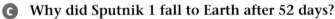

c **Why did Sputnik 1 fall to Earth after 52 days?**

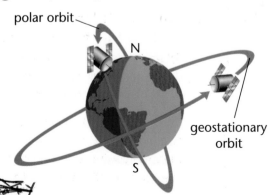

polar orbit

N

geostationary orbit

S

Different orbits

Artificial satellites are put into different orbits depending on the job they are going to do.

Some orbit the Earth at the same speed as the Earth is turning on its axis. These satellites are in **geostationary orbits**. Geostationary satellites orbit the Earth once every 24 hours, which means they stay in the same place over the Earth's surface.

Other satellites are in orbits that take them over the North and South Poles. These are called **polar orbits**.

Uses of artificial satellites

Artificial satellites are useful to us in many ways:

Type of satellite	Uses
communication satellites	Send radio, TV and telephone messages around the world. These are geostationary satellites.
exploration satellites	Carry telescopes and can take clear pictures of planets. They can also look at the universe. The Hubble telescope a good example.
navigation satellites	Used by ships, cars and planes to find their position on the Earth to within a few metres.
observation satellites	Take detailed photos of the Earth. They can show volcanic eruptions, floods and oil spills. They can be used to spy on other countries. They can help predict the weather by observing cloud formations.
space stations	Satellites where astronauts and cosmonauts live and work. The ISS, or International Space Station, has had people in it since November 2000.

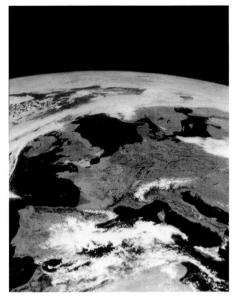

Photo of Europe taken by an observation satellite.

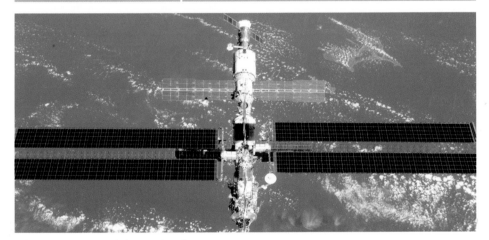

The International Space Station.

Questions

1 a What force keeps satellites in orbit?

   b What happens to a satellite that is travelling too slowly?

2 a What is a polar orbit?

   b What is a geostationary orbit?

   c Suggest a type of satellite that might be in a geostationary orbit and explain your choice.

3 People are launching more and more satellites into space. Why could this cause problems in the future?

For your notes:

● A **satellite** is an object that orbits a larger object. Gravitational attraction keeps fast-moving satellites in orbit.

● **Artificial satellites** are machines launched into space by people. They are used for communicating across our planet or studying space.

● There are **natural satellites**, such as the Earth and other planets orbiting the Sun, and the Moon orbiting the Earth.

J3 The Solar System

Earth at the centre?

Most Ancient Greek thinkers believed that the Earth was the centre of the universe. They thought that the Sun, Moon, planets and stars moved around the Earth. This model was called the **geocentric model** of the universe. 'Geo' comes from the Greek word for Earth. The photo on the right shows this model. It was drawn by an Egyptian astronomer called Ptolemy in AD 200. For over 1000 years this theory was not challenged.

a Where in a geocentric model is:
(i) the Sun? (ii) the Earth?

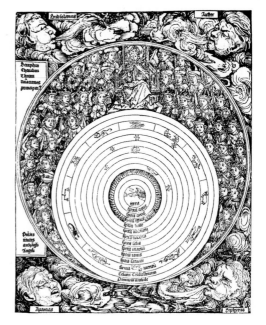

Sun at the centre?

The Polish astronomer Nicolaus Copernicus (1473–1543) said that the Sun was at the centre of the Solar System. He said that the planets go around the Sun in circular orbits. This was called the **heliocentric model**. 'Helio' is from the Greek for Sun. The photo on the right shows this.

Copernicus lived before telescopes were invented. He spent 30 years observing the night sky, just with his eyes. He used these observations as evidence for his model. He had to imagine himself outside the Solar System, looking in. He imagined the different ways the planets could move and decided whether this fitted with his observations.

b Pretend you know nothing about the Solar System. Make a list of some of the evidence that astronomers in Copernicus's time might have observed from looking around them.

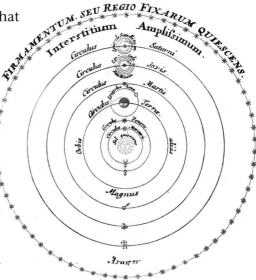

The Italian astronomer Galileo Galilei (1564–1642) made telescopes. These allowed him to see things in space magnified 30 times. He saw that Jupiter's moons orbited Jupiter, not the Earth. This convinced him that the heliocentric model of Copernicus was correct.

c Why was Galileo able to observe Jupiter's moons more accurately than anyone before him?

Galileo demonstrating his telescope.

A dangerous idea

The Roman Catholic Church was very powerful at the time when Copernicus and Galileo lived. It was a crime to openly disagree with the Church's teaching that the geocentric model was 'right'. In 1633, Galileo was put on trial for supporting the heliocentric model. Galileo managed to make a deal with the Church. He told everyone he was wrong and that the geocentric model was correct. He was imprisoned for life rather than executed.

d **The heliocentric model did not go away, even after Galileo said it was wrong. Why not?**

Refining the model

The heliocentric model of the Solar System was improved by many scientists over time.

Tycho Brahe's observatory.

Tycho Brahe (1546–1601) was a Danish astronomer who made very accurate star charts. He included how the planets moved, especially Mars.

Johannes Kepler (1571–1630) was an assistant to Tycho Brahe. Kepler used Brahe's observations to work out that the planets' orbits are ellipses (flattened circles).

The British scientist Isaac Newton (1642–1727) explained Kepler's work in 1687. He showed the relationship between gravitational attraction, the masses of objects and their distance apart.

Sir Isaac Newton.

Questions

1 What is the difference between the geocentric and heliocentric models of the universe?

2 What were the contributions of these people to our present model of the Solar System:

   a the Ancient Greek thinkers?

   b Copernicus?

   c Kepler?

3 Produce a time line to show how ideas about the Solar System have changed.

J4 Birth of the Moon

An odd Moon

Moons orbit planets. Mars has two moons. At the latest count, Jupiter has 50. Most moons are small compared with the planet they orbit. Our Moon is different. It is huge! How did Earth end up with such a huge satellite?

How did it form?

There were three scientific ideas, or theories, of how the Moon formed.

1 *The spin theory*
In 1878 George Darwin suggested that the Moon had been a part of the Earth. When the Earth was young it was very hot and spun very fast. The rock was molten, like hot toffee. Darwin suggested a lump was pulled off by the Sun's gravitational attraction.

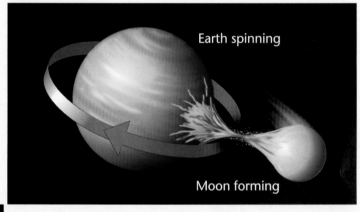

Earth spinning

Moon forming

Earth

Moon starting to orbit Earth

2 *The capture theory*
In 1909 Thomas See suggested that the Moon was 'caught' by Earth's gravitational attraction. In See's theory, the Moon formed somewhere else. It went too close to the Earth and was captured.

3 *The double planet theory*
By the 1950s, most scientists thought that the Earth and Moon formed at the same time. The Moon was so big because it had formed in the same way as the planets had formed. The Earth and Moon were a 'double planet'. This fitted in with scientists' ideas about how planets formed.

Earth

Moon

a Which theory suggests:
  (i) the Earth and Moon formed at the same time?
  (ii) the Moon was made from the Earth?
  (iii) the Moon was formed far away from Earth?

Collecting evidence

Scientists had based their theories on their observations of the Moon from Earth, and on models of how the planets formed. Scientists needed more evidence to decide which theory was correct. In the late 1960s and early 1970s, astronauts went to the Moon and collected rocks. They brought back about 400 kg of Moon rock to Earth.

The Moon rocks were like Earth rocks in many ways. So the Earth and the Moon must have formed together, or close together in space.

b **Which theory does not fit with this new evidence?**

The Moon rocks did not contain any iron. This was odd because the Earth contains lots of iron. Most of it is deep inside, in the core. This suggested that the Earth and the Moon were not formed at the same time in the same way.

c **Would you expect the Moon to have an iron core like the Earth if the 'double planet' theory was correct?**

Suddenly the spin theory was back in fashion because it suggested the Moon was made from the Earth, so the Earth rocks and the Moon rocks would be similar. It also explained that the Moon did not have an iron core, because it had 'spun off' from the surface of the Earth. The surface of the Earth contains a lot less iron than the core.

But there was still a problem. There was no evidence that the Earth had ever spun fast enough to 'spin off' a lump the size of the Moon.

Collecting rock from the Moon.

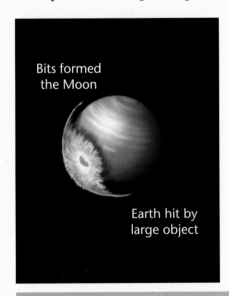

Bits formed the Moon

Earth hit by large object

The giant impact theory

In 1975 two scientists, William Hartmann and Donald Davis, proposed a new theory. They suggested that Earth had been hit by a huge object, the size of a planet. Material from the outer surface of the Earth was blasted off into space. This material formed a ring, that slowly came together to form the Moon. Their giant impact theory explained why Moon rocks were the same as Earth rocks in some ways, but contained no iron.

d **How does the giant impact theory explain the following evidence?**
  (i) **The Moon contains almost no iron.**
  (ii) **The rocks on the Moon are very similar in many ways to the rocks in the outer surface of the Earth.**

Since 1975 many scientists have worked on the giant impact theory. This theory is now accepted by the majority of scientists.

Questions

1 Put these theories in the order they were suggested.

  A the double planet theory

  B the giant impact theory

  C the capture theory

  D the spin theory

2 What extra evidence did the scientists have after 1969?

3 What was the problem with the spin theory?

4 How did Hartmann and Davis use the new evidence to support the giant impact theory?

Learn about:
- Distance and speed
- Time and speed

K1 Racing

First past the post

The athletes in this photo are competing in a 100 m race. The winner is the athlete who crosses the line first. The athlete with the shortest time wins. So speed depends on time. The shorter the time taken, the faster the speed.

a Laura is training for a 400 m race. On Monday she runs 400 m in 45.2 s, on Tuesday in 45.7 s and on Wednesday in 44.7 s. On what day does Laura run fastest?

Furthest wins

Ray and his friends are racing snails. The winning snail is the one that crawls the furthest along the table in 5 minutes, so speed depends on distance. The longer the distance travelled, the faster the speed.

b Fiona's class have built hopping robots. The winning robot is the one that can hop the furthest in 60 seconds. The results are shown in this table. Which robot hops fastest?

Robot	Distance in metres hopped in 60 seconds
Keith's	6.0
Fiona's	3.6
Carolyn's	7.4
John's	7.2
Chris'	1.2

Calculating speed

To work out speed, we need to use distance and time. For example, the winning 100 m athlete Tim Montgomery ran 100 metres in 9.78 seconds.

$$\text{speed in metres per second} = \frac{\text{distance travelled in metres}}{\text{time taken in seconds}}$$

$$\text{Tim's speed} = \frac{100 \text{ metres}}{9.78 \text{ seconds}}$$
$$= 10.2 \text{ metres per second or } 10.2 \text{ m/s}$$

It is very important to include the **units** when you are talking about speed. The units are m/s. Tim Montgomery's speed was 10.2 m/s. If you say just '10.2' you could mean 10.2 miles per hour, which is a slow jog rather than a record-breaking sprint.

Lightning, the winning snail, crawled 1.4 metres in 5 minutes. If we want to compare Lightning's speed with Tim Montgomery's speed, we need to work in the same units. We need to convert the time in minutes to time in seconds. So, 5 minutes is 5 × 60 = 300 seconds. Lightning crawled 1.4 metres in 300 seconds.

$$\text{Lightning's speed} = \frac{1.4 \text{ metres}}{300 \text{ seconds}} = 0.005 \text{ m/s}$$

So Tim Montgomery is about 2000 times faster than a snail!

C Joe runs 100 metres in exactly 10 seconds. What is Joe's speed?

Showing speed

Susan is running an 800 m race. Her coach has four stopwatches and stops one after 200 metres, 400 metres, 600 metres and 800 metres. This graph shows the times for the four distances. We call it a **distance–time graph**.

The slope or **gradient** of the graph shows the speed. The steeper the gradient, the faster the speed. You can see that Susan runs most quickly for the last 200 metres. She covers more ground per second.

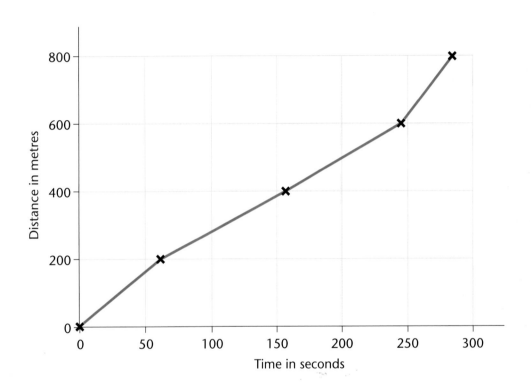

Questions

1 Harriet cycles 200 metres in 20 seconds.

   a How far would she cycle in 10 seconds?

   b How long would it take her to cycle 400 metres?

2 Jenny runs 100 metres in 20 seconds. Which is Jenny's speed?

   100 m   5 mph   5 km/h   5 m/s   20 s

3 Look back at the table of robot results. How fast does Keith's robot hop in m/s? (*Hint*: there are 60 seconds in each minute. Use a calculator if you need one.)

For your notes:

- Speed depends on both the distance you travel and the time you take.

- We work out the speed using 'distance ÷ time'. The **unit** for speed is m/s.

- Speed is shown as a **gradient** on a **distance–time** graph. The steeper the gradient, the faster the speed.

K2 Measuring speed

Measuring distance and time

Each pair of pupils in Janet's class is measuring the speed of sound. Janet and Luisa decide they are going to measure the time it takes a sound to travel the length of the school field.

They choose between the measuring instruments shown in the photo on the right.

Each of the distance-measurers has a different **precision**. The measuring wheel measures to the nearest 1 metre. The tape measure measures to the nearest 1 centimetre. The ruler measures to the nearest 1 millimetre. The ruler is more **precise** than the measuring wheel.

a Luisa chooses the measuring wheel to measure the school field. Do you agree with Luisa's choice? Explain your answer.

b Look at the photos of three watches. Which watch is most precise and why?

Janet chooses the digital stopwatch. Sound travels very quickly. It will cross the field in a very short time. The watch needs to be very precise.

How fast is sound?

Janet goes to the other end of the playing field. She measures the distance with a measuring wheel. She is 300 metres away from Luisa. Luisa has a large wooden clapper. Janet starts her stopwatch when she sees Luisa close the clapper, and stops her stopwatch when the sound reaches her. Janet measures the time as 0.95 seconds.

To work out the speed, Luisa and Janet do this calculation:

speed of sound = $\dfrac{300 \text{ metres}}{0.95 \text{ seconds}}$

= 316 m/s

They tell their teacher, Mrs Brook, that the speed of sound is 316 m/s.

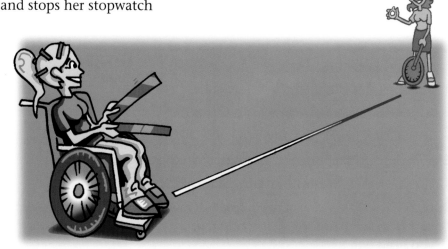

How reliable?

Mrs Brook asks Janet and Luisa how **reliable** their value is for the speed of sound. A value becomes more reliable the more times you measure it.

The two girls are not sure and decide to repeat the experiment five more times, calculating the speed each time. Their results are shown in this table.

Experiment	1	2	3	4	5	6
Time in s	0.95	0.94	0.88	0.92	0.86	0.90
Speed in m/s	316	319	341	326	349	333

Not all their values for the speed of sound are the same. They decide to calculate a **mean** (an average) of their results.

$$\text{mean speed} = \frac{316 + 319 + 341 + 326 + 349 + 333}{6}$$
$$= 331\,\text{m/s}$$

The speed of sound is 330 m/s. By repeating the experiment and working out the mean, Janet and Luisa had a more reliable value for the speed of sound.

C Why did Janet use a stopwatch that measured one-hundredths of a second, rather than her normal watch?

Measuring speed

When we measure speed, it is sometimes not obvious we are measuring both distance and time. A car speedometer measures both the distance travelled and the time taken. Light gates like the ones in this photo can measure speed because there is a clock built into the computer to measure time. We tell the computer the distance between the light gates.

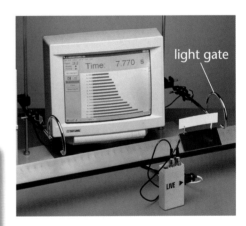

light gate

Questions

1 Match the correct beginnings and endings to make sentences.

Beginnings
Repeating measurements and taking a mean …

A stopwatch is more precise …

To measure speed you need to measure …

Ends
… than a clock with only two hands.

… both distance and time.

… gives a more reliable value.

2 Look at these times. They are the same time measured differently. Put them in order with the most precise first and the least precise last.

   84 706 seconds   **a day**   **1412 minutes**   **23.5 hours**

3 Four pupils have to measure the length of a stick as part of a science challenge. The stick is exactly 83.2 cm long.

   a Which measuring instrument should they use?
   A A 1 m tape measure marked in cm.
   B A 30 cm ruler marked in mm.
   C A 1 m tape measure marked in mm.

   b Describe how they could make sure their measurement is as reliable as possible.

For your notes:

- A more **precise** measuring instrument measures in smaller amounts, for example millimetres instead of centimetres.

- A more **reliable** value comes from repeating a measurement and taking a **mean**.

Steady speed

John plays ice hockey. He is taking part in a science experiment about forces and speed.

John skates around the rink and then glides 10 metres. There are light gates every 2 metres along the glide path. John breaks the beam when he glides past them and a computer records the time.

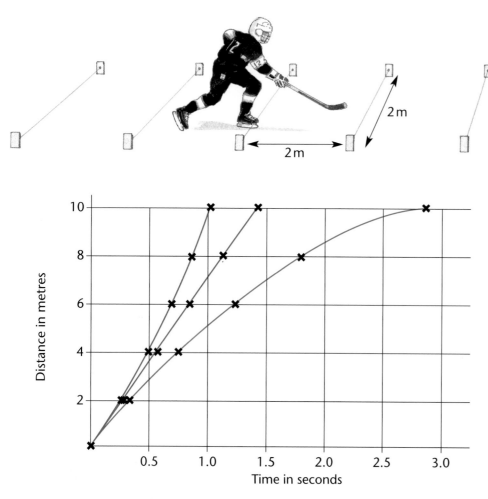

The **blue** line on the graph above shows John gliding through on his skates. The line is straight, with a constant gradient. This means that John is travelling at a **steady speed**. There is almost no friction between the skates and the ice, so he does not slow down.

Speeding up

John then skates through the light gates, pushing as hard as he can against the ice. The **brown** line on the graph shows this.

The graph is not straight. John is not travelling at a steady speed. The slope is getting steeper. This shows us that John's speed is changing. He is speeding up. As time goes on, he covers more distance each second.

ⓐ **John did the experiment again. This time he travelled 4 metres in the first 0.5 seconds.**
  (i) **How far did he travel in 1 second?**
  (ii) **What was his steady speed?**

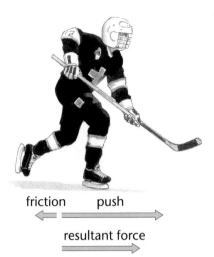

friction   push
⟵   ⟶

resultant force
⟶

John speeds up because he is pushing against the ice. John's push forward is a lot larger than the friction. The forces are unbalanced and John's forward force is larger, so he speeds up.

The blue arrow in this diagram shows the **resultant force**. The resultant force is the overall force. If there is a 100 N force forward and a 10 N force backwards, then there is an overall or resultant force of 90 N in the forwards direction. The resultant force makes John speed up.

Do you remember?

Forces are measured in newtons, N. We show forces using arrows. The length of the arrow shows the size and direction of the force.

Slowing down

Finally, John goes through the light gates on his knees. His ice hockey kit will protect his knees.

The pink line on the graph on page 102 shows John sliding through on his knees. The line is not straight. The slope is getting less steep. This shows us that John's speed is changing. John is slowing down. As time goes on, he covers less distance each second.

friction
⟵

friction
⟵

The forces are unbalanced. There is a force backwards, friction, slowing him down, but no force forwards to balance it. The unbalanced force slows John down.

b **What would make John slow down even more? Give a reason for your answer.**

For your notes:

- Unbalanced forces make objects speed up or slow down.

- Balanced forces make objects travel at a **steady speed**.

- A straight line with a constant gradient on a distance–time graph shows a steady speed. If the slope is getting steeper, this shows speeding up. If the slope is getting less steep, this shows slowing down.

- If the forces are unbalanced, you can work out the size and the direction of the **resultant force**.

Questions

1 Copy and complete these sentences about forces and speed.

  a You travel at a steady speed when …

  b You slow down when …

  c You speed up when …

  d A distance–time graph shows a steady speed when …

2 A skater pushes forward with a force of 30 N. The friction is 5 N.

  a What is the resultant force?

  b Is the resultant force forwards or backwards?

  c Does the skater speed up, slow down, or travel at a steady speed?

Thrust SSC

The world land speed record was broken in 1997 by Andy Green driving *Thrust SSC* shown in this photo. *Thrust SSC* travelled at a mean (average) speed of 763.04 mph.

The force pushing the car forward comes from the car's engines. It is called **thrust**. *Thrust SSC* had two very large jet engines (the type used on planes). Each engine can produce a force of 110 000 N, or 110 kN.

Particles 1

A force backwards, slowing the car down, is caused by friction. When the car moves forward it has to push air particles out of the way. The particles rub against the car, slowing it down. This is called air resistance. Most of the friction is because of air resistance. When a car is moving at 763 mph it has to push past a lot of air particles. The air resistance is huge.

a Name the force: **(i)** forwards and **(ii)** backwards on the *Thrust SSC* car.

Maximum speed

When the car starts up it is moving slowly. It is pushing past fewer air particles than later on, so the air resistance is low. The thrust is much larger than the air resistance. The forces are unbalanced and the resultant force makes the car speed up. This is shown in the left-hand diagram below.

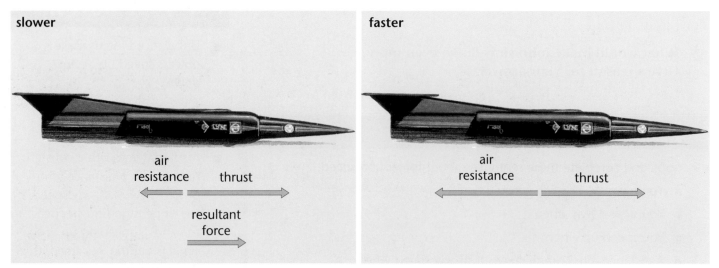

As the car speeds up it has to push past more air particles than before. The air resistance increases. Finally, the air resistance balances the thrust and the car goes at a steady speed. This is its maximum speed. This is shown in the right-hand diagram above.

b Why does the *Thrust SSC* car stop speeding up?

Streamlining

Cutting down the air resistance increases the maximum speed. It means the car can go faster before the air resistance balances the thrust.

Smooth, sleek shapes have lower air resistance and are more **streamlined** than lumpy, boxy shapes. Streamlined shapes push past the particles in the air or water more easily. The designer of *Thrust SSC* made it as streamlined as possible.

The friction between a moving object and water is often called **drag**. Fast-moving objects are often streamlined to reduce drag or air resistance. Aeroplanes push past many air particles when they fly. Boats and submarines push past many water particles.

Look at this photo of a shark. Sharks are streamlined, so that they can swim more quickly after their prey.

Even small bumps on the surface can increase the air resistance or the drag. That's why Olympic swimmers shave off the hair on their bodies and wear caps on their hair.

C Penguins are very streamlined. What survival advantage does this give them?

Special body suits cause less drag than skin.

Questions

1 Match the correct beginnings and endings to make sentences.

Beginnings	Ends
The pushing force of the engine …	… types of friction.
Air resistance and drag …	… to the movement of the vehicle.
Friction acts in the opposite direction …	… thrust and friction are balanced.
Maximum speed is reached when …	… is called thrust.
Air resistance and drag are …	… increase with speed.

2 This table describes the forces on a car.

	Thrust in N	Friction (including air resistance) in N	Speeding up, slowing down, or steady speed
A	200	10	
B	100	150	
C	200	200	

a Copy the table and complete the last column.

b A car goes down a sliproad onto a motorway, travels along the motorway at high speed and then brakes because there is more traffic.

Put A, B and C from the table into the correct order to fit with the car's movement.

3 Racing cyclists wear very tight-fitting clothing and smooth helmets with a wraparound visor. Explain how this helps them go faster.

For your notes:

- The pushing force of an engine is called **thrust**.

- The friction of a vehicle pushing past particles is called air resistance or **drag**.

- Air resistance or drag is larger when a vehicle is travelling faster, because it pushes past more particles.

- Maximum speed is reached when the thrust is balanced by the air resistance or drag.

Stop!

This photo shows a drag racer. Drag racers have engines that give huge thrust, but no brakes. When they cross the finishing line they turn off the engine, but they only have air resistance to slow them down.

Without a parachute, the drag racer would run out of track before it slowed down. By using a parachute, the drag car's air resistance is increased, so it stops in a shorter time.

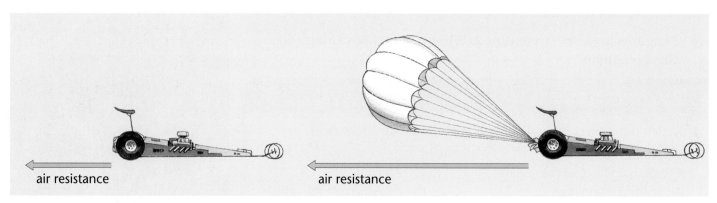

air resistance   air resistance

The parachute increases the air resistance because it 'catches' the air. The air particles hit the parachute, slowing the drag car down.

a Why does the car need a low air resistance during the race?

b Why does the car need a high air resistance after the race?

air resistance

weight

Falling

Look at this photo of a skydiver. She is falling at a steady speed. Her weight is balanced by the air resistance.

If she hits the ground at this speed she will die. She needs to slow down, so she uses a parachute.

When she opens the parachute she is falling quickly. The parachute has a large surface area and catches a lot of air. Millions of particles are trapped in the parachute. The air resistance is very large. The forces are unbalanced and the skydiver slows down. This is shown in diagram A opposite.

As she slows down, the skydiver and her parachute push past fewer air particles. The air resistance decreases. The air resistance and the weight balance, so the skydiver falls at a steady speed. This is shown in diagram B.

The new steady speed is a lot slower than her steady speed without a parachute. She lands at a safe speed, without injury.

c Why does a skydiver with an open parachute have a larger air resistance than before she opens her parachute?

Did you know?

You can investigate how air resistance changes with speed now! Push the flat of your hand through the air. If you push slowly, you feel nothing. If you push fast, you feel the air that you are pushing out of the way.

Putting on the brakes

Normal cars do not have parachutes to show them down. They have brakes. Brakes increase friction.

Ships don't have brakes. They rely on the drag between the water and the ship to slow them down. This works better than it would with a car, because there is more friction between water and the sides of a ship than between air and the sides of a car. Big ships like oil tankers need a huge stopping distance – 20 miles or so!

d Use your knowledge of particles to suggest why there is more friction between water and the surface of a ship than between air and the surface of a car.

Questions

1 a Put these in order of increasing air resistance.
A A skydiver with his parachute open.
B A skydiver, head down, with his arms tight by his sides.
C A skydiver with arms and legs spread out.

b Explain you answer to **a**.

2 Look at this graph. It shows a skydiver falling before she opens her parachute.

a How far does she fall in 5 seconds?

b What is her speed?

c Does her speed change as she is falling? Explain your answer.

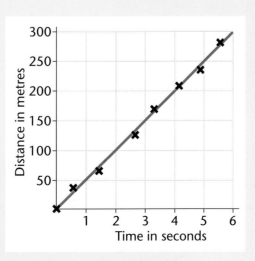

Speeding up

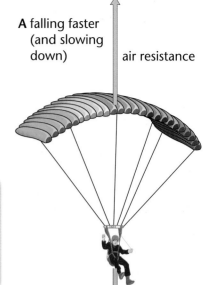

A falling faster (and slowing down) — air resistance — weight

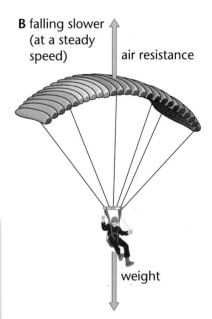

B falling slower (at a steady speed) — air resistance — weight

For your notes:

- Friction slows things down. Increasing friction can stop moving objects.
- Brakes use increased friction and parachutes use increased air resistance to slow things down.
- Parachutes have a large surface area for the air particles to hit.

107

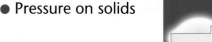

L1 Under pressure

Sinking feeling

Karl and Jackie both have the same weight. They are pushing on the snow with the same force. Karl's boots sink into the snow while Jackie's feet stay on the surface and do not sink.

large area   small area

same weight   same weight

Jackie is wearing snowshoes so her weight is spread out over a larger area. We say that the pressure beneath Jackie's feet is lower than the pressure beneath Karl's feet.

Pressure at the sharp end

When you push a drawing pin into a board, the force from your thumb on the drawing pin is concentrated at its sharp end.

(a) Why does the pin go into the board?

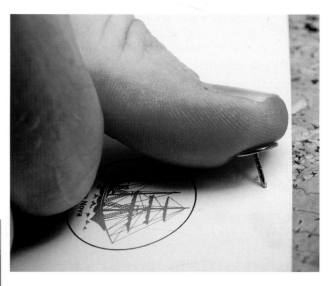

The pressure at the sharp end is very high because the area is so small. The pin is able to move into the board.

(b) Look at the photo below of camels' feet. Why does a camel find it easy to walk on sand?

The area of contact between a sharp knife and a piece of cheese is very small. This means that the pressure is very high. The knife is able to cut into the cheese quite easily.

(c) Explain why a knife does not cut very well when it is blunt.

Pressure and moments

108

What is pressure?

You can see from the examples on the previous page that pressure depends on the force and the area that it is acting on. For the same force:

● if the area is big, then the pressure is low

● if the area is small, then the pressure is high.

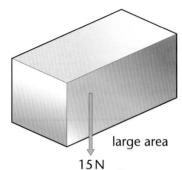

large area

15 N

The block in the diagram on the left is lying on its side with its largest face on the floor.

Now the block is placed on its end. The area of this face is smaller. The force is the same because the block's weight has not changed. The block is **exerting** more pressure.

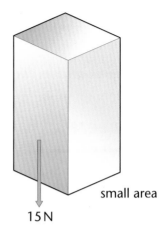

small area

15 N

d What happens to the pressure if you decrease the area a force is acting on?

In a famous circus act, an elephant walked on a woman who was lying down. It didn't hurt at all! The reason was that although an elephant has a huge weight, its feet have a large area. This means that its weight is spread out and the pressure is low.

e Think about a baby elephant and a woman wearing a pair of stiletto heels. Which do you think exerts the higher pressure? Explain your answer.

Did you know?

You can calculate pressure using this equation:

$$\text{pressure (in N/m}^2) = \frac{\text{force (in N)}}{\text{area (in m}^2)}$$

Questions

1 The sentences below explain why the pressure under your feet changes if you wear different types of footwear. Match each beginning with the correct ending. Write down each complete sentence.

Beginnings
If you wear snowshoes …

If you wear stiletto heels …

If you wear trainers …

Ends
… your weight is spread over the same area as your feet.

… your weight is spread over a larger area than your feet.

… your weight is spread over a smaller area than your feet.

2 Karl was watching some people trying to rescue a child who had fallen through the ice into a lake. One person lay flat on the ice and slowly moved forward, the other one tried to walk on the ice. Use the idea of pressure to explain who would be most likely to reach the child.

3 Explain why wading birds that live on sand and mudflats have large feet.

4 Explain why the wheels of a tractor need to be large and wide but the blades on the plough it is pulling are very thin. Use the word 'pressure' in your answer.

5 Explain why people can lie down on a bed of nails without getting hurt.

For your notes:

● The **pressure** depends on the force of an object and the area over which the force is acting.

● For the same force, if the area is big, the pressure **exerted** is low, and if the area is small, the pressure exerted is high.

Taking the plunge

Earth movers

Machines like the digger in this photo can move or lift heavy things very easily.

The digger in the photo has two big syringes that move and put pressure on the liquid inside them.

The big squeeze

Look at the diagram below showing two syringes filled with water. They are joined together by a plastic tube. When plunger A is pushed in, the liquid is put under pressure. Plunger B is pushed out. The pressure acts equally in all directions throughout the liquid. The pressure on plunger B is the same as the pressure on plunger A. The force on plunger B is the same as the force on plunger A.

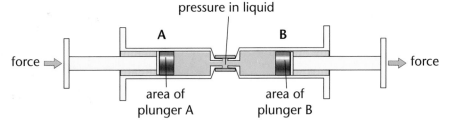

pressure in liquid

force → A B ← force

area of plunger A   area of plunger B

Particles 1

In a liquid the particles are touching each other. You cannot squash a liquid. When you put a liquid under pressure by squeezing it, the particles cannot move any closer together so the pressure is the same throughout the liquid.

a Look at the diagram on the right showing the particles in liquid. Do you think they will be arranged any differently in a syringe full of liquid if you push the plunger in?

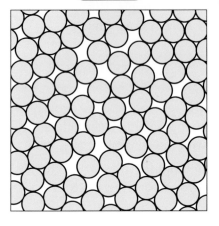

Different sizes

Think what would happen if the two plungers were different sizes. The pressure is still the same throughout the liquid, but the force on each plunger is different. Look at this example.

Plunger A is pushed in with a small force which is spread over a small area. The pressure is the same throughout the liquid. Plunger B has a larger area, but it has the same pressure as plunger A.

b Is the force on plunger B bigger or smaller than the force on plunger A?

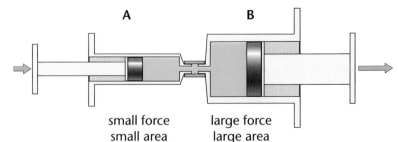

A   B

small force   large force
small area   large area

Because the pressure stays the same, a small force on a small area causes a large force on a large area.

Hydraulic machines

The digger is an example of a **hydraulic machine**. The two liquid-filled syringes are different sizes. A syringe is called a **cylinder** and the plunger is called a **piston**.

If a small force acts on a small input piston, a much larger force acts on the large output piston connected to it.

This is how a hydraulic ramp in a garage lifts a heavy car.

c What can a hydraulic machine do to an input force?

d Name an example of a hydraulic machine.

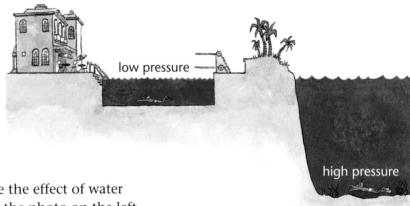

Water pressure

So far we have thought about putting pressure on a liquid from outside. A liquid also has its own pressure inside it, because of its weight. If you swim deep down in a swimming pool, this pressure can hurt your ears. The deeper you go, the heavier the weight of water pushing down on you. This pressure is called **water pressure**.

low pressure

high pressure

You can see the effect of water pressure in the photo on the left. The pressure at the top is lowest so the water is forced out gently. The pressure at the bottom is higher so the water is forced out more strongly.

Did you know?

People can't dive deeper than about 120 m in water because the water pressure would crush them.

Questions

1 Write out each word along with its correct description.

Words	Descriptions
hydraulic system	cannot be squashed because the particles are already touching
water pressure	the force on it depends on the pressure and its area
liquid	the pressure water has because of its own weight
piston	uses pressure in liquids, which is the same in all directions

2 Write a paragraph about water pressure using the following words:

weight   top   bottom   swimming pool

3 When you put your foot on the brakes of a car, a small force acts on a small input piston and a much larger force acts on an output piston connected to it. Which has the larger area, the input piston or the output piston?

4 Explain why the deeper you dive into a pool, the more likely you are to damage your ears.

For your notes:

● Liquids cannot be squashed. The pressure in a liquid acts equally in all directions.

● In a **hydraulic machine**, if a small force acts on a small input **piston**, a much larger force acts on a large output piston connected to it.

● Water has its own pressure. The deeper you go, the heavier the weight of water so **water pressure** increases.

L3 Pressure in the air

Pump it up!

If you have ever played with an old syringe or a bicycle pump, you know what happens if you put your finger over the hole and then push the plunger in. You can feel the gas pressure trying to push your finger off the hole.

Squashing gases

When a force acts on the plunger of a syringe, the plunger moves in a little. It does this because there are big spaces between the particles in a gas, and the particles move closer together when you squash a gas.

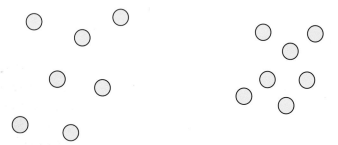

a How does pushing the plunger affect the arrangement of particles in a gas?

When you squeeze a gas in a syringe, its volume decreases. It takes up less space. The number of gas particles doesn't change. They just hit the sides more often so the pressure increases.

- When the volume decreases, the pressure increases.
- When the volume increases, the pressure decreases.

b What happens to the pressure of a gas when you squash it?

The pressure also increases if you pump more air into a fixed volume, because there are more gas particles squeezed together.

c When you pump up a bicycle tyre, does the pressure in the tyre go up or down?

Do you remember?

The particles in a gas are moving around in all directions. They hit the sides of their container. The force of these collisions causes gas pressure.

pressure gauge

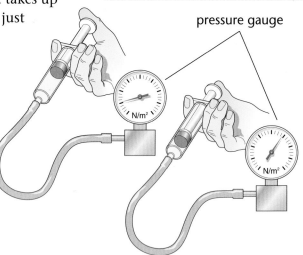

Releasing pressure

If you squash a gas into a small volume and then release it, it expands quickly to fill a larger volume again.

Imagine letting the air out of a bicycle tyre. The air gushes out until the pressure inside the tyre is the same as the air pressure outside the tyre.

Pneumatics

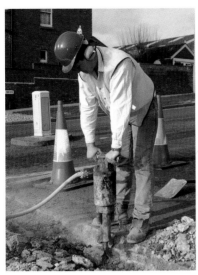

The sudden expansion of squashed gas is used in **pneumatic machines**. They use cylinders and pistons like hydraulic machines, but gas instead of liquid.

A pneumatic drill for breaking up pavements and drilling holes is one kind of pneumatic machine.

Did you know?

'Pneu' is the French word for tyre.

high
pressure

low
pressure

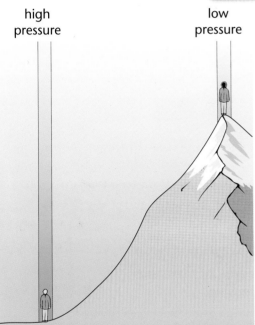

Air pressure

Like water, air has its own pressure inside it which is called **air pressure**. The air pressure changes with depth like water pressure does. The air pressure is greatest on the ground at sea level, because there is a large weight of air above you, pushing down. The higher up in the air you go, the lower the pressure becomes, because the weight of air decreases.

Because air pressure acts equally in all directions and every surface of your body gets an equal share, you usually can't feel its effect.

d Will air pressure be lower or higher at the top of a mountain than at sea level?

For your notes:

- Gases can be squashed because there is space between the particles. This is called gas pressure.

- When a gas is squashed, the volume decreases and the pressure increases. When a squashed gas is released, the volume increases and the pressure decreases.

- The fast expansion of released gases is used in **pneumatic machines**.

- Air has its own pressure. The higher up in the air you go, the lower the **air pressure** becomes, because the weight of air decreases.

Questions

1 Write out each term along with its correct meaning.

Terms	Meanings
air pressure	space taken up by gas particles
pneumatic machines	caused by the weight of air above you
volume of a gas	machines that use a sudden expansion of squashed gas

2 When a balloon has a slow leak, the number of air particles inside is decreasing and they are getting more spread out. Is the pressure inside the balloon increasing or decreasing?

3 Write a paragraph about air pressure on a mountain. Include these words.

weight   top   bottom   climber   mountain

4 Explain how a pneumatic drill works.

L4 Where's the pivot?

Shut the door

Imagine that you are closing a door. First you try to push it close to the hinge, as shown in the picture on the right. Now imagine you push the door shut at the handle. This is much easier. The further away from the hinge you are, the less force you need to turn the door around the hinge.

Pivots are everywhere

Forces can make things turn. Think about the door. It turns around the hinge. A wheel turns around the axle. The **pivot** is the point around which something turns. When you open the door the hinge turns very little but the whole door turns more. It turns because the forces on it are unbalanced.

The joints in your skeleton also act as pivots.

Hinges are pivots.

a Look at this diagram. Which joint is working as a pivot?

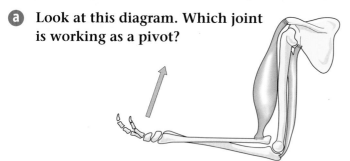

> ## Do you remember?
> Unbalanced forces can make things move forwards or backwards, or make them stop moving.

b Why does the woman in the top picture find it hard to close the door?

If you used to play on a seesaw, you will know that you can lift your friend more easily if you sit far away from the pivot than if you sit close to it.

Holly and Cameron both have the same weight. If they both sit at the ends of the seesaw, they are balanced. But if Holly moves towards the pivot, her end of the seesaw moves upwards. They are unbalanced.

c Why does Holly's end move upwards when she is closer to the pivot?

Levers

To move something around a pivot, you push on a **lever**. When you push on a door, the door is the lever. Your force acts on the end of the lever. To turn a lever around a pivot, the forces on the lever must be unbalanced.

d Look at these photos of opening a tin and using a crowbar. For each one, say what the lever is and where the pivot is.

More distance, less effort

Cameron can lift Holly's weight on the seesaw if he sits further away from the pivot than Holly. The further away from the pivot his force acts, the easier it is to turn the lever and lift Holly.

When you use a lever such as a screwdriver to open a tin, the further away from the pivot your force acts, the less force you need to turn the lever and lift the lid. A long lever makes a job easier.

e Look at these diagrams. Which screwdriver would you use to open the tin more easily?

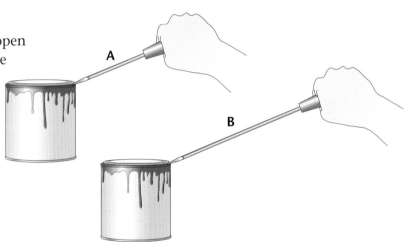

A

B

Questions

1 Which of the following statements are true and which are false? Write out the statements that are true.

  a The longer the lever, the bigger the force that is needed to move an object.

  b It is easier to close a door if you push the door close to the hinge.

  c The shorter the lever, the bigger the force that is needed to move an object.

  d The hinge of a door is its pivot.

  e Joints are examples of pivots.

  f Bones are examples of levers.

2 Look at the photo of a crowbar above. Make a labelled sketch to show the pivot, the lever and where the force is acting on a crowbar.

3 Use the following words to describe why levers are useful.

  pivot   distance   force   longer   less   lever

For your notes:

● A **pivot** is the point around which an object such as a door or a crowbar turns.

● When a force acts on a lever it makes the **lever** turn around the pivot.

● The further from the pivot the force acts, the smaller the force needed to turn the lever.

115

L5 Balancing act

High wire

Look at this photo of a tightrope walker. When he isn't moving the forces on him are balanced. If he begins to topple to one side, he is unbalanced. The pole he holds turns a little. He turns the pole in the other direction to help him to lean the other way to balance himself again. His force on the pole makes it turn. We say his force has a **turning effect** because it makes the ends of the pole turn through part of a circle.

The pole is acting as a lever. Forces act in straight lines.

balanced

turning effect

unbalanced

force

turning effect

force

If he topples this way …

… he moves this side of the pole down.

> ### Do you remember?
>
> When the forces acting on an object are balanced, the object will stay still or it will move at a steady speed.

Rotating doors

Have you ever tried to push a rotating door with someone else pushing harder against you on the other side? They push you backwards so you can't get in.

Cameron is leaning on the rotating door. Mahir is leaning on it with a larger forcer in the opposite direction, so the door is turning. The turning effects of Cameron and Mahir's forces are unbalanced.

ⓐ **Which way will the door turn, away from Cameron or away from Mahir?**

Sometimes the turning effects are balanced. Now Cameron is pushing on the rotating door in one direction and Holly is pushing against him in the opposite direction with the same force. The forces are balanced. The turning effects of their two forces on the door are balanced. The door does not turn.

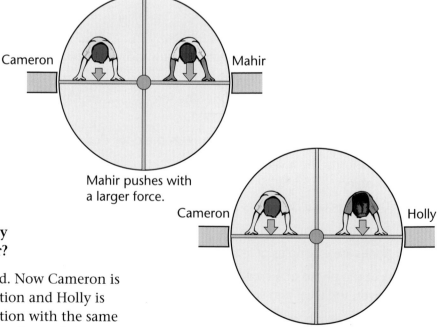

Cameron   Mahir

Mahir pushes with a larger force.

Cameron   Holly

Cameron and Holly push with the same force.

b Look back at the two diagrams of people pushing on the rotating doors. What can you say about the distance from the pivot that they are pushing?

The turning effect of a force depends on the distance from the force to the pivot and on the size of the force acting. The turning effect of a force is greater when the force is acting further away from the pivot.

Balanced systems

Cameron and Holly are sitting on a seesaw. They are the same weight and sit the same distance from the pivot. This means the turning effects on either side of the pivot are the same, so Cameron and Holly balance and the seesaw doesn't turn.

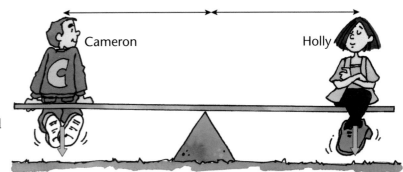

Unbalanced systems

Mahir is heavier than Cameron. They are sitting the same distance from the pivot. The seasaw turns. Look at the diagram.

c Which turning effect is bigger, Cameron's or Mahir's?

d How could Cameron move to balance the seesaw?

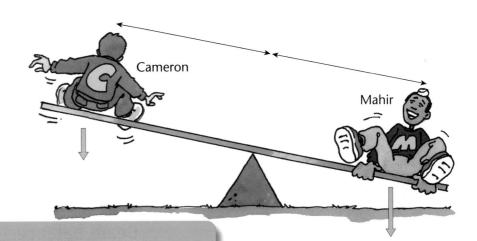

Questions

1 Write out each word along with its correct example.

Words	Examples
balanced system	gets bigger when the force acts further away from the pivot
unbalanced system	two girls of the same weights sit opposite each other on a seesaw, both the same distance from the pivot
turning effect	two boys of different weights sit opposite each other on a seesaw, both the same distance from the pivot

2 Mike sits at one end of a seesaw and balances Ken at the other end. Both of them weigh the same.

a What can you say about the distance the two boys are from the pivot?

b What would happen if one of the boys was heavier?

3 James and Eleanor are on a seesaw. James weighs 50 N and Eleanor weighs 40 N. They are both sitting 2 m from the pivot. Whose weight would have the bigger turning effect?

For your notes:

● The **turning effect** of a force depends on the size of the force acting and the distance from the force to the pivot.

● When two turning effects are unbalanced a lever moves. When they are balanced a lever stays still.

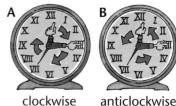
A   B
clockwise   anticlockwise

Watch the clock

Look at the two clocks. On clock A, the hands are going round in the way we normally see. We say they are turning **clockwise**. On clock B, the hands are going in the opposite way from normal. They are turning **anticlockwise**.

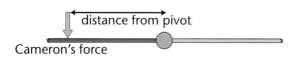
distance from pivot
Cameron's force

a In which direction is the turning effect of Cameron's force acting, clockwise or anticlockwise?

A question of balance

We can look at the turning effects of forces to understand how and why everyday machines work. The turning effect of a force is also called the **moment**.

On a lever such as a seesaw, there are clockwise and anticlockwise turning effects or moments. You can see these in the diagram and table on the right. A small force on a long lever can balance a large force on a short lever. The result is that the moments on both sides balance.

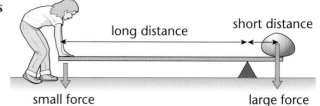
long distance   short distance
small force   large force

Anticlockwise moment of person's force	Clockwise moment of rock's force
small force	large force
long distance	short distance

Beam balance

A beam balance is like a crane. We can check it will balance by doing a simple calculation for each side of the beam. The calculation uses the equation:

size of a moment = force × distance from pivot

On the anticlockwise side there is a force of 2 and the distance from the pivot is 3. The anticlockwise moment is 6.

On the clockwise side there is a force of 3 and the distance from the pivot is 2. The clockwise moment is 6.

The anticlockwise moment and the clockwise moment are both the same, so the beam will balance.

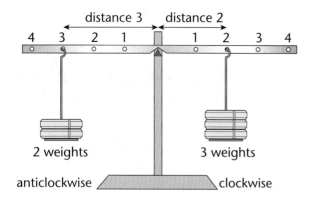
distance 3   distance 2
4 3 2 1   1 2 3 4
2 weights   3 weights
anticlockwise   clockwise

b To balance the beam, what would you have to do to the distance on the anticlockwise side if you took one of the weights off that side?

Counterbalance

We have seen how the turning effects of forces working in opposite directions can be either balanced or unbalanced. This is important to people who use cranes, for example on building sites or to load ships. The photo shows a crane picking up a heavy weight. The crane has a large weight called a **counterbalance** at the other end of the arm. This balances the load and stops the crane falling over.

c When the crane is holding the load high in the sky, what is balancing the load and stopping it from falling?

Human pivots

In your body, your bones meet at joints. The joints are the pivots for the bones to turn around. The bones are the levers. Long bones make good levers.

d Look at the skeleton on the right and list as many places as you can where there are pivots.

Lifting safely

It is very important to lift and move objects safely. To reach down to the object you want to lift, you must bend your knees. Then use your knees and hips as pivots to help you straighten up, as shown in these photos. Don't just bend your back to pick up the object. Bending the back while lifting puts a big force directly on the back and can damage it.

e Name some other situations where you could hurt your back by lifting without bending your knees.

Questions

1 Write out each word along with its correct meaning.

Words	Meanings
moment	point around which a lever turns
counterbalance	turning effect of a force
pivot	weight which stops something falling over

2 Would holding a weight at arm's length need more or less strength than holding it close to your body?

3 Write a paragraph about how to lift objects safely using the following words.

bend   pivots   knees   back   damage

4 Explain the following statements.
   a Tightrope walkers balance themselves with a pole.
   b Longer legs are usually better for picking up heavy objects.

For your notes:

- The turning effect of a force is also called a **moment**.

- When anticlockwise and clockwise moments are balanced an object will not turn.

- A **counterbalance** is a weight which stops something falling over.

L7 Getting balanced

Number balances

Mustapha was using a beam balance. He wondered why it balanced sometimes but not at other times. He experimented with 1 N weights. When the beam is balanced, it is in **equilibrium**.

a Look at these diagrams A and B. What four things affect whether the beam is in equilibrium?

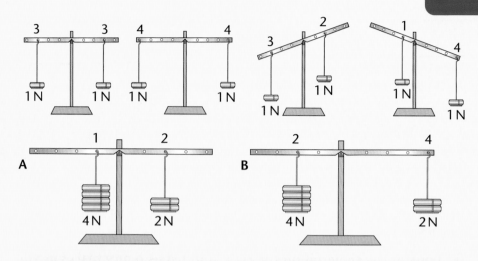

More than one weight

Next Mustapha decided to use more than one 1 N weight on each side and see what happened. He made this table to show what combinations of weights he used to balance the beam.

	Left-hand side		Right-hand side	
	Distance	Weight in N	Distance	Weight in N
A	1	4	2	2
B	2	4	4	2

b Look at the variables in balance A. What happens to make the two sides balance?

c Look at balance B. Does the pattern you found work for this one too?

Mustapha then decided to use 4 N and 8 N weights. He made another table to show the ways he found of balancing the weights.

d Do the combinations Mustapha found follow the pattern you described in question b?

	Left-hand side		Right-hand side	
	Distance	Weight in N	Distance	Weight in N
A	1	8	2	4
B	2	8	4	4
C	2	4	1	8
D	4	4	2	8

Mustapha took a 2 N weight for the left-hand side and a 3 N weight for the right-hand side. He tried out some different combinations to see if they balanced. He made this table.

e Which row do you think will give a combination that will balance? Give a reason for your choice.

	Left-hand side		Right-hand side	
	Distance	Weight in N	Distance	Weight in N
A	1	2	1	3
B	2	2	1	3
C	3	2	2	3
D	4	2	3	3

f Mustapha started row E of his table with a 2N weight at a distance of 5. Write down row E following the pattern.

g Look at these two balances. To make them balance, what mass would you hang: (i) at 4? (ii) at 2?

(i) 2 ... 4 ... 4N ... ? (ii) 3 ... 2 ... 2N ... ?

Equilibrium

There are four variables that you can change to get the beam in equilibrium:

- weight on left-hand side
- distance from weight to pivot on left-hand side
- weight on right-hand side
- distance from weight to pivot on right-hand side.

The beam can be balanced by lots of different combinations of these four variables.

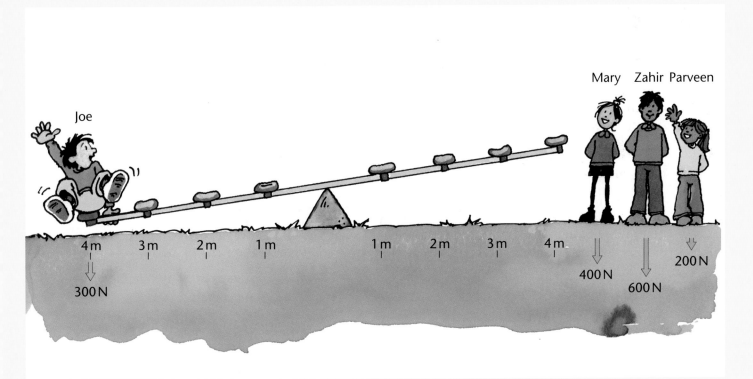

Think about a seesaw. When no one is on the seesaw it is level. It is in equilibrium. Joe sits on the seesaw. It is no longer in equilibrium.

h It is possible to get the seesaw back in equilibrium in many different ways without Joe moving. Think of as many ways as you can. (*Hint*: in some cases three children are on the seesaw.)

i If Joe can move are there any other ways of balancing the seesaw?

Questions

1 A balance has five holes on either side. A weight of 4N is hanging from hole 5 on the left-hand side. Think of all the combinations on the right-hand side that might balance this.

2 Explain to your partner what 'equilibrium' means.

From cells to organs

Do you know the basics?

Cells

All living things except for viruses are made up of small building blocks called **cells**. Cells are small. You need a microscope to see them but they are much bigger than atoms. There are two main types of cell: **animal cells** and **plant cells**. These have a lot in common, but there are also some differences.

Animal cells

Animal cells, like the one shown below, have three main parts: the **cell membrane**, the **nucleus** and the **cytoplasm**.

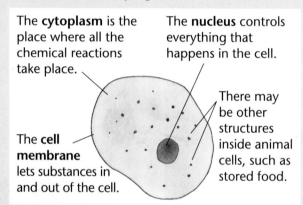

The **cytoplasm** is the place where all the chemical reactions take place.

The **nucleus** controls everything that happens in the cell.

There may be other structures inside animal cells, such as stored food.

The **cell membrane** lets substances in and out of the cell.

Plant cells

A plant cell, like the one shown below, also has a cell membrane, a nucleus and cytoplasm. Unlike animal cells, it also has a **cell wall**, **chloroplasts** and a **large vacuole**.

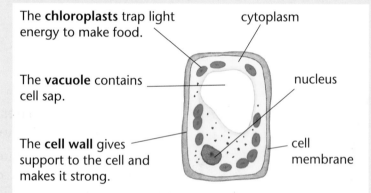

The **chloroplasts** trap light energy to make food.

cytoplasm

The **vacuole** contains cell sap.

nucleus

The **cell wall** gives support to the cell and makes it strong.

cell membrane

Tissues

When a group of similar cells carries out a particular function we call this group a **tissue**.

● Examples of tissues in animals include muscle tissue and nerve tissue.

● Examples of tissues in plants include onion skin tissue and palisade tissue.

Organs

When a group of two or more tissues work together they form an **organ**.

● Examples of organs in animals include the heart, lungs, stomach, eyes and brain.

● Examples of organs in plants include leaves, stems, roots and petals.

Organ systems

When a group of organs work together they form an **organ system**.

● The organs that work together to digest your food make up the **digestive system**.

● Your lungs and tubes that take gases in and out of the lungs are an organ system called the **respiratory system**.

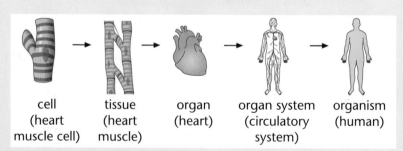

cell (heart muscle cell) → tissue (heart muscle) → organ (heart) → organ system (circulatory system) → organism (human)

● The heart, blood vessels and blood are part of the **circulatory system**.

● The male and female sex organs make up the **reproductive system**.

● All the bones in the body are part of the **skeletal system**.

● A flower is an example of an organ system in a plant.

Are you ready for the next step?

ⓐ A plant cell has parts that an animal cell does not have. Name two of these parts.

ⓑ For each of the following, decide whether it is a part of a cell, a type of cell, a tissue, an organ or an organ system:

(i) heart   (ii) skeleton

(iii) chloroplast   (iv) sperm

(v) leaf

ⓒ Give one example of a cell, a tissue, an organ and an organ system for (i) plants and (ii) animals.

Do you really understand?

All cells **respire** to release energy for life processes.

The success of an organism depends on what happens in every cell and on all the organ systems working together to carry out life processes.

For example:

- The reproductive system is an organ system that makes sure that offspring are produced that are similar to their parents.
- The digestive system is an organ system that makes sure that large food molecules are broken down into small food molecules that can be absorbed into the blood and used by the body.

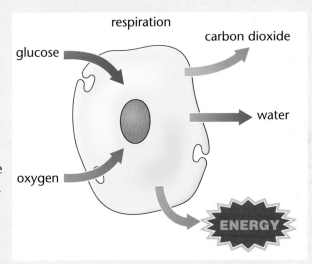

1 Copy the table and rearrange the words to match each organ system with the description of the life process it carries out.

2 Write one or two sentences using the words below to explain clearly the function of the heart.

| blood | respiration | cells | oxygen | circulation |

System	Description
digestive system	releasing energy from food for cells to use
reproductive system	breaking down food so the body can use it
respiratory system	producing offspring
circulatory system	transporting substances to all cells in the body

3 Write one or two sentences using the words below to explain clearly the function of the stomach.

| food | enzymes | molecules | digest | blood |

4 Write one or more sentences using the words below to explain clearly the function of the lungs.

| oxygen | alveoli | carbon dioxide | blood | respiration |

5 Explain why chloroplasts are found in leaf cells but not in root cells.

Interconnections

Do you know the basics?

Food chains

Food chains show who eats what. When animals eat plants, and animals eat other animals, energy is transferred from one to the other. You can see how this happens when you draw a food chain. The arrows show the direction of the energy transfer. Energy enters all the food chains from the Sun through photosynthesis. This means that everything depends on the Sun and plants to survive.

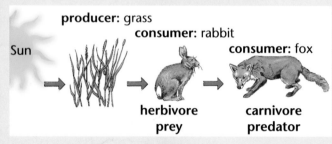

producer: grass
consumer: rabbit
consumer: fox
Sun
herbivore prey
carnivore predator

Pyramids of numbers

To show the number of each species in a food chain, we draw a **pyramid of numbers**. Bars of different lengths represent the numbers of organisms.

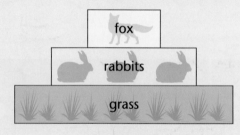

fox
rabbits
grass

Food webs

Organisms in one food chain are often in other food chains too. By drawing food chains linked together in a **food web**, you can see how energy flows through all the organisms that live in one place.

Humans are like any other animal – we are members of lots of different food chains and food webs.

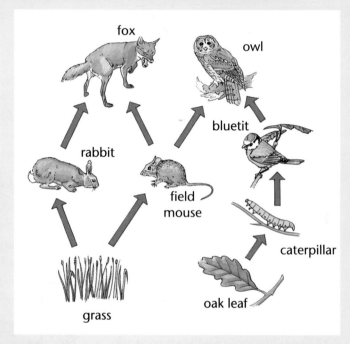

fox
owl
bluetit
rabbit
field mouse
caterpillar
grass
oak leaf

Are you ready for the next step?

a A lion eats a zebra which eats grass. Write a food chain to show this.

b Look at the food web on the right. By starting at the bottom and following the arrows, try to write out as many food chains as you can from this food web.

c Explain where the energy in food chains comes from, and how it is transferred along a food chain.

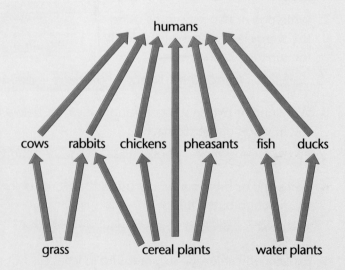

humans
cows rabbits chickens pheasants fish ducks
grass cereal plants water plants

Do you really understand?

Organisms are like batteries. They store energy in their bodies as biomass. As energy is transferred from one member of a food chain to the next, energy often leaves the food chain. This is because all the biomass at one stage of the food chain is not converted to biomass in the next stage of the food chain:

● Some of it is eaten by animals in other food chains.

● Some of it is used in respiration to give energy for movement and other life processes.

● Some of it is lost as heat.

● Some of it is lost as waste.

● Some of it is not eaten, such as the bones of animals or the hard bits of plants, and some organisms die and are not eaten.

Farmers work with food chains that include humans. If they can reduce the amount of energy that leaves between the stages of the food chain, and if they can increase the amount of energy entering the food chain in photosynthesis, they can make more food for humans, and more money for themselves.

1 After a very rainy, cloudy summer, Mrs Jones found her wheat crop was much smaller than in the previous hot summer.

   a Explain why this happened by thinking about the energy the crop received each year.

   b Greenhouses often use artificial lights. Explain how this can change the energy in the food chain and increase the amount of the crop.

2 Look at this tree. Suggest why all the energy is not passed on from one organism to the next in the food chain shown below.

   oak tree → greenfly → bluetits → sparrowhawks

3 Look at the food web below.

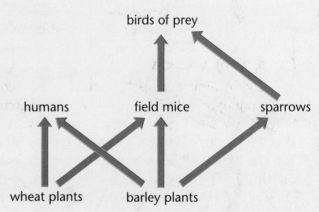

   a If you were a farmer, which animals would you want to remove so that more wheat plants can be eaten by humans?

   b What effect would this have on the number of birds of prey?

   c How would the change in the number of birds of prey affect the number of sparrows?

   d A farmer does not like killing small mammals, and plants more wheat and barley plants instead. This way he thinks he'll still get the crop yield he needs, even if some of the plants are eaten. Why is this not a long-term solution?

Physical changes

Do you know the basics?

Made from particles

Everything is made from tiny **particles**. The three **states of matter** – **solids**, **liquids** and **gases** – behave in different ways because their particles are arranged differently.

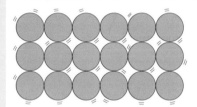 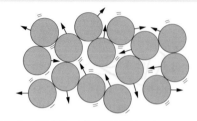 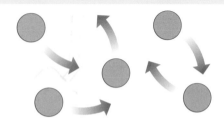

● In a solid, the particles are very close together. They are held together quite strongly in a regular pattern.

● In a liquid, the particles are close together. The particles are not held together as strongly as they are in a solid and are not in a pattern. They can slide over one another.

● In a gas, the particles are very far apart. The particles are not held together, so they move quickly and randomly in all different directions.

Dissolving, expanding, gas pressure and diffusion can all be explained using particle movements.

Changes of state

When ice melts a physical change happens. You turn ice into water. You can then boil the water and turn it into water vapour. Both **melting** and **boiling** are physical changes. A melting solid takes in energy. This is transferred to the particles and they move faster.

When a liquid boils, more energy is transferred to the particles and they move even faster. If you let water vapour cool it **condenses** back to water. If you **freeze** water it changes to ice. The changes are **reversible**. No new substances are made.

Are you ready for the next step?

ⓐ Draw labelled diagrams to show the particles in a solid, a liquid and a gas.

ⓑ Write out each description of how the water particles are moving and match it with one of the words below.

solid   liquid   gas

(i)   They slide over each other and change position.
(ii)   They move quickly and randomly in different directions.
(iii)   They vibrate.

Do you remember?

Evaporation happens at the surface of a liquid where only some of the particles gain enough energy to change into a gas. Evaporation takes place at any temperature, not just at the boiling point.

c Look at these pictures.

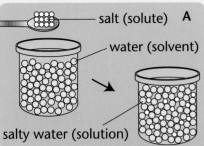

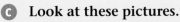

Copy and complete this table to match each picture with the best description. The first row has been done for you.

Description	Picture
When a solid *dissolves* in water the solvent particles surround the particles of the solid. The solid is broken up.	A
The particles in a gas are moving in all directions and constantly hitting the walls of their container. Every time a particle hits a wall there is a tiny push. The sum of all these pushes is called *gas pressure*.	
Diffusion happens in gases and liquids when particles spread out and mix with other particles.	
An increase in temperature makes the particles move more and they take up more space. This is called *expansion*.	

Do you really understand?

1 For each event listed below, choose one of the words below to describe what is happening.

boiling   evaporating   condensing   melting   freezing

a Washing drying on a line outside.

b A child shivering by pool.

c Making ice cream.

d Pouring hot water on frosted car window.

e Snowman disappearing in the Sun.

2 These pairs of particle diagrams on the right show changes of state. For each diagram, A to E, say what the drawing represents: solid, liquid or gas. The first one is done for you. A shows a solid going to a liquid.

3 Jane pumps up a bicycle tyre.

a Explain how the gas molecules inside the tyre exert pressure on the walls of the tyre.

b What happens to the number of gas particles in the tyre as is it is pumped up?

c How does the number of gas particles in a tyre change when the tyre gets a puncture?

Do you remember?

Particles themselves do not change size.

d The mass of a solution is the same as the mass of solvent + solute. Mass is conserved when you make a solution.

(i) If you dissolve 10 g of sugar in 200 g of water, what will be the mass of the solution?

(ii) How could you get the sugar back?

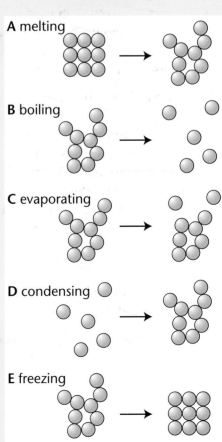

A melting

B boiling

C evaporating

D condensing

E freezing

Chemical changes

Focus on particles 2

Particles 2

Do you know the basics?

What are substances made of?

Atoms are the simplest type of particle that exists. Atoms cannot be broken down any smaller.

Molecules are groups of two or more atoms chemically combined together. They can be made up of just one type of atom or more than one type.

An **element** is made up of only one type of atom. Examples of metallic elements include copper, iron, mercury and zinc. Oxygen, hydrogen and sulphur are non-metallic elements.

A **mixture** contains more than one substance physically mixed together. Examples of mixtures are air and sea water. Mixtures can be separated by filtration, chromatography and distillation.

A **compound** is a substance that is made up of more than one type of atom chemically joined together. Examples of compounds include water, iron oxide and sodium chloride. The elements in a compound can be rearranged by chemical reactions.

When you burn magnesium it reacts with oxygen in the air to make magnesium oxide. This is a **chemical change**. During a chemical change you make new substances. The magnesium has gone. It has changed into magnesium oxide. It is an **irreversible** change. You cannot turn magnesium oxide back into magnesium. Chemical changes happen when the atoms in the **reactancts** are rearranged to form new substances, the **products**.

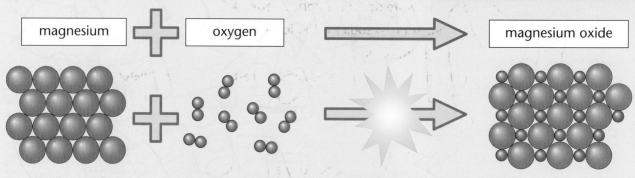

Are you ready for the next step?

a (i) Are iron and sulphur elements or compounds?

(ii) How could you separate a mixture of iron filings (small pieces of iron) and sulphur?

b (i) If you heat a mixture of iron filings and sulphur they react to form iron sulphide. Can you separate the iron and the sulphur now? Explain your answer.

(ii) Is iron sulphide an element, a mixture or a compound?

Do you really understand?

Chemical reactions

There are some types of chemical reaction you need to know about.

Displacement

A more reactive metal can push a less reactive metal out of a compound.

zinc + copper oxide → zinc oxide + copper

Oxidation

Oxygen may react with metallic or non-metallic elements to produce an oxide.

carbon + oxygen → carbon dioxide

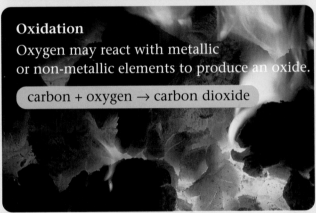

Combustion

This is a reaction between a fuel and oxygen.

methane + oxygen → carbon dioxide + water

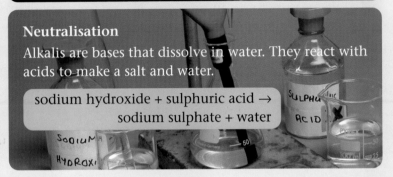

Neutralisation

Alkalis are bases that dissolve in water. They react with acids to make a salt and water.

sodium hydroxide + sulphuric acid →
    sodium sulphate + water

Patterns in chemical reactions

There are patterns in some chemical reactions that form compounds. We can write general word equations for them.

A   metal + oxygen → oxide

B   metal + sulphur → sulphide

C   metal + acid → salt + hydrogen

D   carbonate + acid → salt + carbon dioxide + water

E   acid + base → salt + water

F   oxide + acid → salt + water

1 Copy the word equations a–f below. Use the general word equations above to help you classify each reaction. For each, write down the correct letter A–F.

  a hydrochloric acid + sodium hydroxide → sodium chloride + water

  b magnesium + oxygen → magnesium oxide

  c calcium carbonate + hydrochloric acid → calcium chloride + carbon dioxide + water

  d copper oxide + sulphuric acid → copper sulphate + water

  e iron + sulphur → iron sulphide

  f _____ + sulphuric acid → _____ + hydrogen

2 Use the general word equations above to help you to copy and complete the word equations below.

  a hydrochloric acid + _____ → potassium chloride + water

  b iron + oxygen → _____

  c copper + _____ → copper sulphide

  d magnesium oxide + _____ → magnesium sulphate + _____

  e sodium carbonate + hydrochloric acid → _____ + _____ + water

3 Sally held a strip of copper 4 centimetres long in a Bunsen burner flame. There was a green tinge to the flame and black copper oxide was formed on the surface of the metal. Write a word equation for this reaction.

Forces all around

Do you know the basics?

Forces are pushes, pulls or twists. Forces have both size and direction. We measure forces in **newtons, N**, and we show them as arrows. The length of the arrow shows the size of the force and the arrowhead shows its direction.

Forces act in pairs and work in opposite directions. If the forces are of equal size, but in opposite directions, they are balanced. Look at the forces on the snowmobile and the skydiver. They are **balanced**. The snowmobile and the skydiver are travelling at a steady speed, neither speeding up nor slowing down. When you stand still, the forces are also balanced, as shown in the third cartoon below.

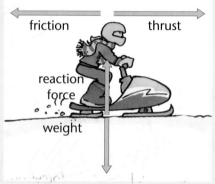

Thrust is pushing the snowmobile forward and **friction** is holding it back.

Weight is pulling Freda down and **air resistance** is acting the other way.

Weight pulls Freda down and the **reaction force** stops her falling through the floor.

If one of the forces in the pair is bigger, then the forces are **unbalanced**. Unbalanced forces cause speeding up and slowing down.

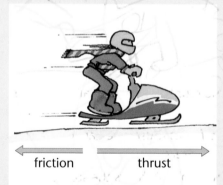

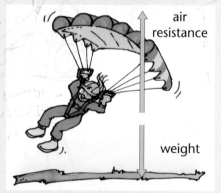

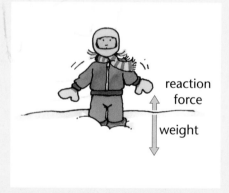

The snowmobile is **speeding up**

Freda is **slowing down:** she is still falling but her downwards speed decreases.

The reaction force from the snow is less than Freda's weight, so she sinks.

The *difference* between the size of two unbalanced forces is called the **resultant force**. For example, if the thrust on the snowmobile is 900 N and the friction is 800 N, there is a 900 − 800 = 100 N overall force pushing forwards. The snowmobile speeds up.

Unbalanced forces can also cause a change in direction. If the wind blows as Freda skydives, she will drift sideways as well as falling. If the snowmobile is traveling along a slope, its weight may make it slide sideways.

Are you ready for the next step?

ⓐ Use your ideas about pairs of forces to explain the following:
(i)   Why does the parachute slow Freda down?
(ii)   Why does Freda sink in the soft snow?
(iii) Why doesn't Freda sink through the floor?

ⓑ The snowmobile is moving at a steady speed. What does this tell you about the thrust and the friction?

ⓒ The snowmobile's thrust is 800 N. How large is the friction force?

ⓓ Freda hits a patch of poor snow. The friction increases to 960 N. The thrust stays the same, 800 N. Which is larger, the thrust or the friction?

ⓔ Will Freda speed up, slow down, or travel at a steady speed now?

ⓕ The resultant force on the snowmobile is 960 – 800 = 160 N. Does this resultant force act backwards or forwards now?

ⓖ Freda increases the thrust to 1050 N to get through the poor snow. If the friction is still 960 N, what is the new resultant force on the snowmobile now?

ⓗ What will happen to Freda's speed now?

Do you really understand?

1 Freda goes cycling. In the picture below she is zooming along at a steady speed.

a Name four forces acting on Freda.

b Draw your own diagram of Freda showing these four forces. Label the forces in your diagram.

c Explain, using your ideas about forces, what Freda must do to speed up.

d Explain why Freda wears a suit and helmet that make her more streamlined and decrease air resistance.

2 Freda goes scuba diving. Four of the forces on Freda are weight, drag, thrust and upthrust.

a Identify the four forces A, B, C and D in the drawing.

b Which two forces must be balanced for Freda to float in the water?

c Look at this table. It shows the sizes of A, B, C and D at three different times. Describe Freda's movement at (i), (ii) and (iii).

Force	A	B	C	D
(i)	800 N	0	800 N	0
(ii)	1000 N	0	800 N	0
(iii)	800 N	400 N	800 N	200 N

Focus on energy

Making things happen

Do you know the basics?

Energy makes things happen.

Energy can be **transferred**.

Light energy, sound energy, movement energy, heat energy and electrical energy are all energy on the move.

Energy can be **stored**.

Strain energy.

Chemical energy.

Gravitational energy.

We measure energy in **joules**, **J**, or **kilojoules**, **kJ**. 1000 J = 1 kJ.

Are you ready for the next step?

Look at the cartoon of the boy at the party above.

a Which object is giving out:
(i) light energy?
(ii) sound energy?
(iii) thermal (heat) energy?

b Which object has a lot of kinetic (movement) energy?

c Which objects take in electrical energy to make them work?

Look back at the three cartoons showing stored energy.

d Which part of the pogo stick stores strain energy?

e How do you know that there is chemical energy stored in the match?

Do you remember?

Another way of saying heat energy is **thermal energy**. Another way of saying movement energy is **kinetic energy**.

Do you really understand?

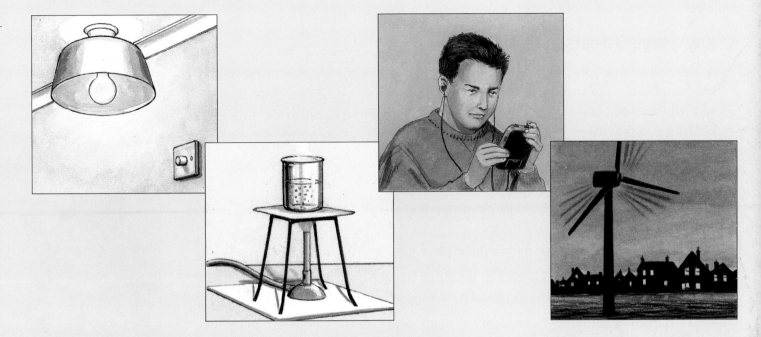

1 Which device in the drawings above:

   a takes in kinetic energy and produces electrical energy?

   b takes in electrical energy and gives out light energy and thermal energy?

   c uses a store of chemical energy and gives out thermal energy and light energy?

   d transfers energy from a store of chemical energy to electrical energy and then to sound energy?

Look at the drawing of the boy with the Walkman. The Walkman stops working because the batteries are flat.

2 Explain why the batteries are flat. Use the word 'energy' in your answer.

Look at the drawing of the electric lamp. It has a dimmer switch. Turning the dimmer switch changes the amount of current going to the lamp.

3 The brightness of the lamp is turned down.

   a Has the current increased or decreased?

   b What has happened to the energy going to the lamp?

4 Think about two Bunsen burners. Each heats 200 cm³ of water. One has the gas on full. The other has the gas tap half-way, letting less gas through.

   a Which beaker of water will boil first?

   b Explain your answer using the word 'energy'.

Look at the drawing of a wind turbine. It generates electricity. Wind is a renewable energy resource.

5 What is the advantage of wind over non-renewable energy resources like coal, oil and natural gas?

6 Compare how the wind turbine works on two days. On one day there are strong winds. On the other day there is only a gentle breeze. Use the word 'energy' in your answer.

133

How to revise

Key Stage 3 tests

At the end of Year 9 you will do a Key Stage 3 test which covers everything you have studied over the last three years. It is an opportunity for you to show how much you have learned over the course. To help you get a good mark and feel confident about doing the test, it is a good idea to revise thoroughly before the test. Your teacher will probably help you with this in your science lessons, but there is a lot you can do yourself.

Where to revise

- It is best to revise in a room with no distractions like a TV, music or people busy doing other things.

- Most people find it best to have a quiet place for revising.

- Use a table or desk which gives you plenty of space to lay out your books and notes.

- Make sure you have a good source of light to read by.

- Get yourself organised – have plenty of blank paper and a selection of pens and pencils in different colours as well as the notes or books you need.

When to revise

- Try to set aside some time early each evening. Don't leave it too late so that your brain is tired.

- Revise for about 15 minutes and then take a 5-minute break. You could perhaps allow yourself to listen to a song (only one!). Then do another 15 minutes' revision and have another short break. Revise for another 15 minutes, and then have a longer break.

- Breaking up your revision into small chunks like this is much better than revising for a solid hour without any breaks. You will remember more this way.

- Keep a clock close by to help you keep track of the time.

What to revise

You may have already worked through the six double-page booster spreads to help you fully understand the five key ideas in science (cells, interdependence, particles, forces and energy). Even if you have, we suggest you work through them again to improve your knowledge of these key ideas so you can explain other topics.

The four revision spreads have SAT questions with notes from an examiner giving you suggestions about how to help you focus your revision on answering SAT questions.

You need to understand ...	... to understand and explain ...
cells	reproduction, photosynthesis and digestion
interdependence	food chains, food webs and energy transfer
particles	the properties of solids, liquids and gases, diffusion and pressure in gases and liquids
particles	what atoms and molecules are made of, how substances react to make new substances
forces	why things move, change direction or speed or balance, and how planets orbit the Sun
energy	how energy is transferred to make things happen, how electrical devices work and how things heat up and cool down.

Revision timetables

- Don't try to revise your entire science course in one night!
- Plan your revision long before your test.
- Work out how you will divide the material up, and how much you will revise each night.
- Work out how many evenings you will have available for revision.
- Make a timetable something like this to make sure you cover every topic at least once.

Day	What I will revise	Tick when done
Day 1	Topic 1	
Day 2	Topic 2	
Day 3	Topic 3	

How to revise

There are many different techniques that you can use. Here are just a few.

1 Read – Cover – Write – Check

Read an entire double page spread in the book. Then close the book and write notes on as many key points as you can remember. Then open the book again, check what you wrote down and go over the things you didn't remember. Repeat this until you can remember everything on the pages.

2 Make a memory map for each section. Then try to learn the memory map – think about the way each part of it is linked together. Then cover the map up and try to redraw it.

3 Write out lots of questions. Then close the book and see if you can answer them. You can also get someone else to ask you the questions. On the next few pages there are example test questions with tips from the examiners about the best way to answer.

4 Make sure you know the meanings of all the key words you come across.

5 Make up silly rhymes or mnemonics for important facts or patterns. The sillier they are, the easier it will be for your brain to remember them.

Don't just sit there with a book in front of you. It's not the best way to learn. The best way to revise is by actively doing tasks to make your brain work. This will make it much easier to remember things. Then you can go into your test confident that you will do the best you can.

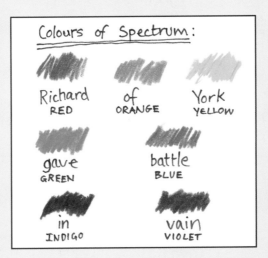

Colours of Spectrum:

Richard — RED
of — ORANGE
York — YELLOW
gave — GREEN
battle — BLUE
in — INDIGO
vain — VIOLET

135

Scientific enquiry example questions

The example questions show you how to write good answers to make sure you always get all the marks available.

The main reasons why pupils do not do as well as they should is that they give answers that are too general, or that are incomplete and do not give a full answer to the question.

Do not fall into this trap. Read these extra comments around the questions for useful tips that will help you to get all the marks and make sure you are successful in your KS3 Test.

a The factor you observe or measure is often called the dependent variable. The other variable – the one you change – is time, and is called the independent variable.

b Get the time interval right, otherwise you may miss details that are important.

c There are always factors you need to keep the same to make the test fair. This factor is called the control variable.

d When plotting graphs, you need to plot the factors on the correct axes. The factor you measure nearly always goes on the vertical axis.

e This is another factor that will make the test fair.

12 Katie carried out an experiment about evaporation.

She wrapped a paper tissue around the bulb of a thermometer, using a rubber band to hold the tissue. She dipped the thermometer into a liquid and then removed the thermometer. She took readings of the temperature.

She replaced the tissue and repeated the experiment with a different liquid.

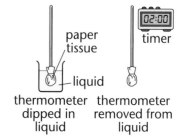

paper tissue   timer

liquid

thermometer dipped in liquid   thermometer removed from liquid

a What factor did Katie measure to collect her results? (1)

<u>Temperature</u> ✓

b Jade said that the readings should be taken every 10 minutes, but Katie said it should be every 2 minutes.

Why would Katie's time give more reliable results? (1)

<u>The smaller time interval would show up changes</u> ✓

c Write one factor Katie should keep the same to make the test fair. (1)

<u>Same amount of tissue paper</u> ✓

d Here are Katie's results. She is going to use them to plot a graph.

| Time in minutes | Reading on the thermometer in °C | |
	Water	Ether
0	23	23
2	21	11
4	20	–2
6	20	–8
8	20	–1
10	20	8
12	20	17

On which graph axis should she plot the time? (1)

<u>The horizontal (x) axis</u> ✓

e Why did Katie replace the tissue each time she used a different liquid? (1)

<u>To make sure any liquid left on the tissue did not</u> <u>interfere with the experiment</u> ✓

Total (5)

13 David had some crushed ice in a beaker. He had taken it from a freezer.

He put a thermometer into the ice. He heated the beaker gently for 10 minutes.

He measured the temperature of the ice every minute.

Here are his results:

Time in minutes	0	1	2	3	4	5	6	7	8	9	10
Temperature in °C	−6	0	2	4	8	16	28	40	53	65	77

a Use the graph paper below to plot David's results. (2)

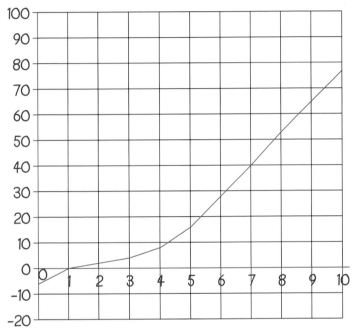

b Label the graph axes on the lines given. Give the units. ✓ (2)

c Draw a smooth curve to connect the points on the graph ✗ (1)

Total (5)

a There are two marks here. The first is for plotting the points correctly.

The second is for plotting the axes the correct way round. The factor you measure nearly always goes on the vertical axis.

Make sure you label the axes correctly and give the correct units.

c David has made a very common mistake. He has joined each point to the next, so the graph line is not a smooth curve.

This graph line shows how a smooth curve should look. Drawing it like this will also show up any points that do not fit the pattern.

Temperature in °C (vertical axis)

Time in minutes (horizontal axis)

Biology example questions

2 The diagram shows a plant cell.

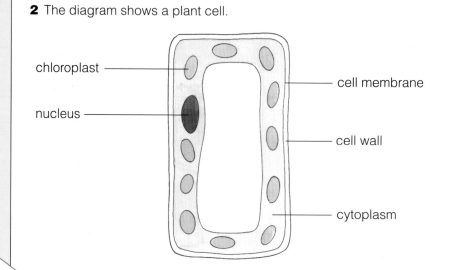

a The cell is called a palisade cell. It makes up the tissue under the upper surface of the leaf. This is one of several types of cell you need to know about and to recognise in diagrams.

a Where in the plant would you find this type of cell? (1)

In the leaf ✓

b Most animal and plant cells have a nucleus. Give two other parts, labelled on the diagram, which are present in both animal and plant cells. (2)

Part 1 Cell membrane ✓

Part 2 Cytoplasm ✓

b Remember, plant cells have chloroplasts, a cell wall and a large vacuole, which animal cells don't.

c i What is the function of the cell wall? (1)

To give shape to the cell ✓

ii What is the function of the chloroplasts? (1)

Photosynthesis occurs in the chloroplasts. Carbon dioxide and water are converted into glucose and oxygen ✓

Total (5)

c i The cell wall is made of cellulose. It provides support for the plant cell. Cell walls do not hold the cell contents together – this is the function of the cell membrane. Cell walls allow plant cells to stack together to make the plant.

c ii 'Photosynthesis' is the word that will get you the mark. Do not write 'to make food for the plant', as this is too vague.

Light is absorbed by the chlorophyll in the chloroplasts. This provides the energy for the photosynthesis reaction.

4 Ben copied the following information from the labels of two packets of food.

Food	Energy in kJ/100 g	Protein in g/100 g	Fat in g/100 g	Sugar in g/100 g	Fibre in g/100 g	Vitamin C in mg/100 g
X	424	6.9	0.6	3.6	6.2	0
Y	736	20.2	10.6	0	0	0

a Food Y contains a smaller variety of nutrients than food X. Give **two** reasons why food Y might be chosen instead of food X as part of a balanced diet. (2)

Reason 1

The rest of the person's diet might be low in protein ✓

Reason 2

The person could be underweight or ill and need a high energy intake to build them up ✓

b Ben made a curry. The label on the curry power showed:

	Calcium in mg/100 g	Iron in mg/100 g	Vitamin C in mg/100 g
curry powder	640	58.3	0

i Give one reason why calcium is needed by the body. (1)

For healthy bones ✓

ii Give one reason why iron is needed by the body. (1)

To make red blood cells ✓

c With his curry, Ben also had:
boiled rice; chopped-up, boiled egg;
a glass of water; a slice of lemon.
Which one of these foods provided Ben with vitamin C? (1)

Lemon ✓

Total (5)

a The question 'Why choose food Y?' requires reasons or explanation to be given.

You need to make comparisons between food X and food Y in order to give reasons why you would choose Y. Just stating 'Food Y is much higher in energy, protein and fat' is a poor answer.

b i 'Strong *or* healthy bones *or* teeth' is a good, complete answer.

Writing the word 'bones' or 'teeth' would probably get you the mark, but the question asks for a reason.

b ii Iron is needed to make in red blood cells. If you do not have enough iron you become anaemic.

Do not write just 'blood' or 'blood cells' – this does not give enough detail to get you the mark.

c Vitamin C comes from fruit, particularly citrus fruit such as lemons and oranges.

Chemistry example questions

a These terms are ones you need to remember.

Remember that water melts and freezes at its melting point.

Water boils and condenses at its boiling point.

3 Water can exist in three physical states: ice, water and steam.
  a What is the name given to the process that changes: (2)
    i ice into water? ....melting.. ✓
    ii steam into water? ...condensing.. ✓

  b A beaker of ice was placed in a warm room. The graph shows how the temperature in the beaker changed from the start of the experiment.

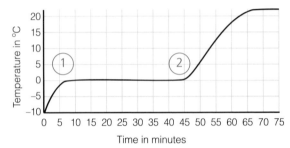

How long after the start had all the ice just gone? (1)
..45... minutes

b Look at the graph.
  ① The ice starts to melt after about 6 minutes.
  ② The temperature does not start to go up until all the ice has melted at 0°C.

  c Draw diagrams, in the boxes below, to show the arrangement of water molecules in ice, water and steam. Use circles, like this ○, to represent the water molecules.

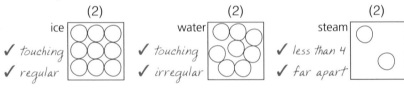

  d Water is a compound of two elements. A diagram of a water molecule is shown below. In this diagram the circles represent atoms.
  In the circles, write the correct symbols for the elements. (1)

Total (10)

c You will get two marks for each drawing. The ticks show what you will get the marks for.

Remember to draw circles at the size indicated. Try to draw them roughly the same size. You will lose a mark if they are of very different sizes.

The particles in solids are regularly arranged and close packed. The circles can alternate rather than lining up, e.g.

The particles in liquids are random or irregular, but close packed. You cannot squeeze a liquid into a smaller volume. In your drawings make sure there are not too many spaces and that each circle touches at least two other circles.

Gases are mainly empty space with particles racing about and bouncing off each other. Show no more than three circles in your drawing.

d The formula for water is H_2O. If you think about the number of atoms here, the two smaller circles must be Hs for hydrogen and the larger one must be O for oxygen. You are not expected to remember this shape but you ought to be able to think out the answer.

5 Alex has four solids. They are labelled **W, X, Y** and **Z**. He adds a sample of each one to some dilute acid. The table shows his results.

Solid	Result with dilute acid
W	it reacts slowly and gives off hydrogen
X	it reacts quickly and gives off carbon dioxide
Y	it dissolves and the liquid becomes warm
Z	it remains undissolved as a white powder

a i Which solid could be chalk (calcium carbonate)? (1)

X ✓

ii Give the name of another rock which reacts with acid in the same way as chalk. (1)

Limestone ✓

b i One of the solids is a metal. State which one and give the reason for your choice. (2)

W because it gives off hydrogen with acid ✓

ii The list below gives five metals.
copper   gold   potassium   sodium   zinc
Write them in order of reactivity starting with the most reactive. (1)

Most reactive Potassium Sodium Zinc
Copper Gold Least reactive ✓

iii Give the name of another metal which would react with acid in a similar way to zinc. (1)

Iron ✓

c As each of the solids reacts, the acid is used up. Describe a test you can use to show whether or not acid is still present. (2)

Add universal indicator. ✓ It turns from green to red if acid is present. It stays green if the acid has been used up ✓

Total (8)

a i All carbonates react with acid to give carbon dioxide.

a ii Chalk and limestone are sedimentary rocks made of calcium carbonate. Marble is another correct answer. Marble is a metamorphic rock made of calcium carbonate.

b i With acid, reactive metals give off hydrogen. They react to form the metal salt. The more reactive they are, the faster they react.

b ii You need to know a reactivity series, e.g.

potassium
sodium
calcium
magnesium
aluminium
zinc
iron
[hydrogen]
copper
silver
gold

Notice hydrogen is in the series to link it with reactions with acids. A metal above hydrogen will react with acids to give hydrogen gas. A metal below hydrogen will not.

c To get the second mark you need to show the result of the test if the acid is still present, as well as the result if the acid is used up.

Writing 'Use indicator' would not get you a mark unless it was obvious from the colour changes you gave which indicator you meant.

b iii If you know your reactivity series, questions like this are very easy. The metal just above or just below zinc will react in a similar way. Metals above aluminium will react much more quickly, and metals below iron will not react.

Physics example questions

a When choosing an answer from a list, always copy correctly and completely. Do not shorten 'reaction of the ground' to 'reaction'.

b The symbol for the unit of force is N (capital). The word is newton (without a capital letter).

c These answers always require a sentence. You need to include the link that to get faster needs a bigger forward force.

If you were unsure about the name of force B, an answer like 'The force from Jack's hand is larger than force B' is acceptable because it uses the information from the diagram.

Do not write 'It is bigger' because the marker does not know what 'it' refers to.

8 Jack is pushing a luggage trolley along level ground at an airport.

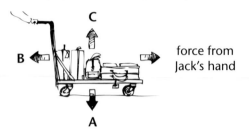

There are four forces acting on the trolley.

a One of the forces is the push from Jack's hands. The others are friction, weight and the reaction of the ground.

Complete the sentences. (3)

Force A is **weight** ✓

Force B is **friction** ✓

Force C is **reaction of the ground** ✓

b What are the units in which force is measured? (1)

newtons ✓

c The trolley is moving forwards, and it is getting faster. One pair of forces is now unbalanced.
Compare the sizes of these two forces. (1)

The forward force of Jack's hand must now be bigger than the backward force of friction ✓

d Jack has to push the trolley 150 m to the check-in desk.
If he pushes the trolley at 3 m/s, how long will it take him? (1)

$$\text{Speed} = \frac{\text{distance}}{\text{time}} \qquad 3 = \frac{150}{?}$$

$$\text{therefore } ? = \frac{150}{3} = 50\,s \checkmark$$

Total (6)

d In any calculation, write down the equation in the form that you remember it and put the numbers in. Then rearrange the equation. Use small numbers to help you check your rearranged equation. For example, $3 = \frac{6}{?}$ is easier to rearrange than an equation with letters involving algebra.

Many speed calculations can be done using common sense rather than the formula:

$$\text{speed} = \frac{\text{distance}}{\text{time}}$$

It always pays to check your answers using common sense. Think to yourself: if it goes 3 m in 1 second then it goes 30 m in 10 seconds or 90 m in 30 seconds. So it goes 150 m in 50 seconds. Do not forget the units!

11 a The Earth is the third planet from the Sun.

   i Which is the second planet from the Sun? (1)

   Venus ✓

   ii Which is the fourth planet from the Sun? (1)

   Mars ✓

b The diagram shows the orbits of the Earth and Mercury. Mercury takes 88 Earth-days to orbit the Sun.

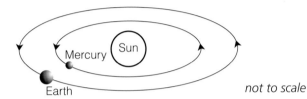

not to scale

In the diagram, the Earth and Mercury are lined up with the Sun. How long will it take before the Earth and Mercury are lined up with the Sun again? Tick the correct box. (1)

less than 88 Earth-days ☐

exactly 88 Earth-days ☐

more than 88 Earth-days   ✓

exactly 365 Earth-days ☐

c Mercury and Pluto are both small rocky planets. Mercury is one of the brightest objects in the night sky, but Pluto is so faint that it cannot be seen with the naked eye.

Give **two** reasons why Mercury is much brighter than Pluto. (2)

Reason 1

Mercury is nearer the Sun so gets more light than Pluto ✓

Reason 2

Earth is nearer Mercury than Pluto so light has less distance to travel after being reflected ✓

Total (5)

a You need to remember the order of the planets in the Solar System from the Sun, at least to Jupiter: Mercury; Venus; Earth; Mars; Jupiter; Saturn; Uranus; Neptune; Pluto.

b Mercury takes 88 days to get back to the same place (where it is shown on the diagram). In this time the Earth will have moved on about one-quarter of an orbit so Mercury will have to cover at least another quarter of its orbit to catch up with Earth.

c The further light, or any form of energy, has to travel, the more the light or energy spreads out.

Mercury is nearer to the Sun than Pluto. It receives much more light. Light also has less distance to travel from Mercury to Earth than from Pluto to Earth, so spreads out less. Good answers include both parts of the explanation.

Glossary

acid rain Rain polluted by acidic gases such as sulphur dioxide dissolved in it. Acid rain is more acidic than rainwater that is not polluted.

addictive Likely to cause addiction – that is, a need to keep taking a drug. Without the drug, an addicted person feels ill.

air pressure The gas pressure caused when air particles all around us hit us and other surfaces.

anomaly Something that is more than, less than, or different to what is normal or expected.

anticlockwise Moving in a curve in the same direction as the hands of a clock.

artificial insemination Semen is put into the female's vagina through a long tube to make her pregnant without sexual intercourse.

artificial satellite A satellite that is made by people, such as a communications satellite.

bone The hard tissue that makes up the skeleton.

cartilage A smooth substance found on the ends of bones, which allows them to move over each other easily.

chlorophyll A green substance in plants that is needed for photosynthesis.

circulatory system An organ system that transports substances around the body.

clockwise Moving in a curve in the opposite direction to the hands of a clock.

compete Try to get the same food sources or other resources as other organisms.

conduct To pass along or through. Thermal (heat) energy can be conducted. Electricity can be conducted.

conserved Energy – energy is conserved: it is not created or destroyed, but just passes from place to place. We call this 'conservation of energy'.

conserved Mass – stays the same. In all chemical reactions, the mass of substances is conserved.

contract Get shorter. When a muscle gets shorter, we say it is contracting.

counterbalance A weight used to balance another force, that stops something falling over.

cylinder Part of hydraulic and pneumatic machines that acts like a plunger, moving in and out of a cylinder.

desirable feature A feature that is useful, that you would choose to pass on in selective breeding.

displacement reaction A chemical reaction in which an element is removed from its compound by a more reactive element.

dissipated Spread about. Energy such as light or heat is dissipated from a source to the surroundings.

distance–time graph A graph that shows the speed of a moving object – the distance travelled for each unit of time.

drag The friction force between a moving object and the air or water particles it is moving through.

drug Any substance that changes how your body works, or alters the way you think and feel.

energy efficiency How much energy a device wastes. Something with low energy efficiency wastes lots of energy.

equilibrium When the forces on an object are balanced, it is in equilibrium.

estimate An informed guess, usually applied to numbers.

exert When you exert pressure on something, you apply a force to it.

extinct A species that becomes extinct dies out completely.

fertiliser A substance used to keep soil fertile, so that plants have all the mineral salts they need to grow.

fit/fitness Being in good health, and able to carry out the body's functions efficiently.

fluid A liquid found inside joints that allows the bones to move easily.

generator A device that takes in kinetic (movement) energy and turns it into electrical energy.

genes Instructions that control the way our features develop. Genes are passed on from parents to offspring.

geocentric model A model of the universe with Earth at the centre and everything, including the Sun, moving around it.

geostationary orbit The path around the Earth taken by a satellite travelling at the same speed at which the Earth rotates.

global warming An increase in the average temperature of the Earth.

gradient The slope of a line on a graph.

gravitational potential energy The energy stored because something is lifted up.

heliocentric model A model of the Solar System with the Sun at the centre and the planets moving around it.

hydraulic machine A machine that works by transferring pressure through a liquid.

hydrocarbons A substance that contains only carbon and hydrogen atoms.

illegal drugs Drugs that harm the body and are banned by law.

insecticide A type of pesticide that kills insects.

interact When two or more things have an effect on each other.

joint A place in the skeleton where bones can move.

leaf A plant organ that is important for photosynthesis.

lever A simple machine for lifting objects, that turns around a pivot.

ligament Strong tissue that holds bones together at a joint.

mean The average of a set of values or measurements.

medical drugs Drugs given by a doctor or pharmacist to help make someone better.

milk yield The amount of milk a cow produces.

moment The turning effect of a force around a pivot. The moment of a force depends on the size of the force and its distance from the pivot.

monitor To check and measure over a period of time.

muscle Tissue of muscle fibres that can contract (shorten). A muscle is an organ made of muscle tissue and other tissues such as capillaries.

natural satellite A satellite that is made by nature, such as the Moon orbiting the Earth.

non-selective Affecting everything. Non-selective insecticides kill all insects, not just the pests.

ore A rock containing a metal or a metal compound.

organic Not involving the use of manufactured chemicals.

oxide A compound formed when a substance burns and joins with oxygen in the air.

pesticide A chemical used on crops to kill insects or other pests.

pests Destructive insects or other animals that attack crops, food or livestock.

phlogiston A substance supposed by eighteenth century scientists to be contained by anything that burns, and that is released by burning.

photosynthesis Plants make food by photosynthesis. They turn carbon dioxide and water into sugars and oxygen, using light energy.

piston Part of hydraulic and pneumatic machines. Pistons move inside cylinders.

pivot The point around which a lever turns.

pneumatic machine A machine that works by transferring pressure through a compressed gas.

polar orbit The path taken by a satellite passing over the North and South Poles of the Earth.

pollution The contamination of water, air or soil by harmful or toxic substances.

precise Accurate, or as close as possible to an exact amount or detail.

pressure The effect of a force spread out over an area.

probability The chance of an event happening.

raw material The basic material or natural substance from which something is made, such as metal ore.

reactive A reactive substance takes part in chemical reactions, usually quickly and releasing lots of energy.

reactivity series A list of metals arranged in order of reactivity, with the most reactive at the top.

recreational drugs Legal drugs such as caffeine, alcohol and nicotine taken for enjoyment.

red blood cells Special cells that carry oxygen around the bloodstream.

relax When a muscle stops contracting we say it relaxes. It gets longer and thinner.

reliability How much something can be trusted. A value becomes more reliable the more times it is measured.

respiratory system An organ system that takes oxygen into the blood and gets rid of carbon dioxide from the blood.

resultant force The size of an unbalanced force, which makes the object move, or speed up, or slow down.

root A plant organ that takes in water and minerals from the soil, and anchors the plant in the soil.

root hairs Tiny structures on a root that absorb water from the soil.

salt A substance formed in a neutralisation reaction.

satellite An object that orbits a larger object.

selective Affecting some things and not others.

selective breeding Choosing parents with desirable features to produce new varieties of animals or plants that have these desirable features.

self-pollinated When the nucleus of the egg cell in a flower is fertilised by the nucleus from the male part of the same flower.

side effect An additional, often undesirable, effect of a drug on the body of the person who takes it.

skeleton A system of bones that protects and supports your body and allows you to move.

sprain Stretch a ligament enough to cause swelling and pain.

steady speed Not getting faster or slowing down, but keeping at the same speed.

strain Stretch or pull a muscle enough to cause pain.

streamlined A shape of an object that allows it to move through the air easily. A streamlined car has low air resistance.

tendon Tissue that connects muscles to bones.

thrust The pushing force of a rocket or engine.

turbine A device for changing movement in one direction into spinning movement.

turning effect When there is a force on an object and the force arrow is to one side of the pivot, the force has a turning effect on the object.

unit A standard quantity by which something is measured.

unit of alcohol The amount of alcohol in half a pint of beer, a glass of wine or a measure of spirits.

unreactive An unreactive substance does not take part in chemical reactions, or does so only slowly.

veins In plants, these transport water, minerals and sugars around the plant.

voltmeter An instrument used to measure voltage.

water pressure The pressure in water. It is caused because water pushes on objects from all sides as the water particles collide with the object.

weedkiller A chemical substance applied to weeds, that kills them.

weeds Plants that grow where you don't want them to grow.

Index

Note: page numbers in **bold** are for glossary definitions